MARIJUANA

MARIJUANA

E. R. BLOOMQUIST, M. D.

GLENCOE PRESS

A Division of The Macmillan Company

Beverly Hills

Collier-Macmillan Limited, London

First printing, 1968.
Second printing, 1968.
Third printing, 1969

Library of Congress catalog card number: 68-54641.

Glencoe Press
A Division of The Macmillan Company.
Collier-Macmillan Canada, Ltd., Toronto, Canada.

Printed in the United States of America.

To Lila, Carol, Roger, and Donald
who patiently waited . . .

CONTENTS

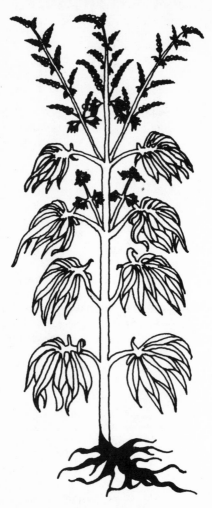

Illustration of cannabis, or hemp, from the works
of Dioscorides, first century after Christ.

(From Robert P. Walton's *Marijuana: America's New Drug Problem*. Philadelphia: J. B. Lippincott, 1938.)

FROM CANNABIS TO MARIJUANA 1

Some call it evolution,
And others call it God.
—William Carruth

It's what's happening—marijuana, leading the list of the mind-expanding drugs, the easiest to acquire, the cheapest, the most widely used, and the safest. And what is this thing called marijuana? How does one know it and understand it?

Long before marijuana became something smoked by the boy next door, it was an easily propagated weed growing abundantly in subtropical and temperate climates. In the eighteenth century the great Swedish father of botanical classification, Carl von Linné (Linnaeus), gave marijuana the genus and species name of *Cannabis sativa L.* And so it is technically known today. Users refer to it as "pot," "Mary Jane," or "grass," or any one of a myriad of other names. For purposes of clarity, however, we shall refer to it as cannabis or marijuana.

Although the present controversy over cannabis is one concerning the *use* of a substance obtained from the cannabis plant, it is necessary to know something about the plant and its growth pattern if we are to understand the nature and activity of its product. Accordingly, in this first chapter we shall examine the botanical facts about cannabis, its growth and cultivation, the appearance of the plant in its growing state, the preparation of the characteristic product marijuana, some medical effects of marijuana use, and the pharmacology of cannabis. A tall order, to be sure, but necessary if we are to understand how a wild weed has become a symbol of the turned-on generation.

1

Cannabis is unique. It exists in a single species, although there are a number of varieties. The varieties differ from one another in the quantity and potency of the resin they produce. These differences are largely conditioned by geographical location of plant growth. *Cannabis indica,* for instance, contains the most potent resin of the varieties. This resin (which Americans commonly call hashish) is five to six times more intoxicating than the resin of the varieties *Cannabis americana* or *Cannabis mexicana,* both of which are most commonly used in the United States.

The name *cannabis* is Latin for "hemp," or canelike plant, and denotes the genus of the hemp family of plants. *Sativa,* the species name, is Latin for "planted or sown," and denotes the nature of the plant's growth (from seed, not from perennial roots). *Indica, americana,* and *mexicana* refer to the varieties of the single species *Cannabis sativa* and indicate the difference among the varieties which occurs as they grow in various geographical regions. Thus *Cannabis sativa indica* is the form native to India. It is an interesting botanical fact that if one takes *Cannabis indica* seed and transplants it to the United States, both *Cannabis indica* and *Cannabis americana* will spring from the planting. In a few short generations, however, because of climatic and soil conditions, the *indica* variety will completely disappear, leaving only the *americana* to continue the reproductive cycle.

Cannabis as a plant is more commonly known as hemp. As such it has a long history of commercial usefulness. Among industrial growers hemp is seldom thought of as a source of psychotoxins. Rather, it is commercially the source of an oil which is an ingredient of various paints, varnishes, and linoleum, while the plant itself serves as a basic substance for the production of twine, rope, bags, clothing, and certain papers.

Although the botanical terms place cannabis in the hemp genus, further classification is open to dispute. Some botanists insist that hemp belongs to the mulberry family Moraceae, which also includes the sycamore. Others feel its uniqueness

2

justifies establishing a separate single-member botanical family, which they term Cannabinacae. But all agree that the same plant that produces hemp and various industrial byproducts is the plant that produces marijuana.

GROWTH AND CULTIVATION

Cannabis is an herbaceous annual, that is, a leafy plant with little or no woody parts which grows for a season, dies down, then springs up again the following year from its own seed. The seed is essential, since cannabis will not regrow from last season's roots. Cannabis is dioecious; it requires both a male and a female plant to reproduce itself. Both sexes have flowering tops and both produce resin that has psychotoxic (mind-intoxicating) properties. The male, however, is essentially useless to those who want to acquire the psychotoxic effects of the resin because what little resin is in its body is difficult to obtain. The male plant can, however, be used as a substitute for tobacco and may be smoked in either cigarettes or pipes with minimal psychotoxic effect.

The male and female cannabis plants look very much alike to the casual observer, but their reproductive functions become quite specific as the plants mature. When the male plant blossoms it produces flowers that open wide, exposing pollen-laden stamens, the tiny life-bearing male anthers. The female also produces flowers containing an inconspicuous pistil, or egg-bearing female flower, which patiently awaits the arrival of the pollen. The female plant must depend upon a properly directed wind to bring the pollen to her. Other plants can rely on insects for the transportation of their pollen. Not cannabis. Insects steadfastly refuse to have anything to do with the plant. So cannabis is quite literally propagated by the breeze. Once a capricious wind has wafted the pollen to the female, reproduction begins, mature seeds form and fall to the ground, and the cycle begins again.

The female of the species is the hardier of the two. The male, once it has served its reproductive purpose, dies. Under controlled agricultural circumstances the male does not even die naturally. Growers yank it out by the roots once pollination has occurred. In India where cannabis cultivation has been highly developed, the male never gets the chance to pollenate the female—the plant is destroyed once it begins to show its sex. The Indians provide a "ganja" (marijuana) doctor who travels up and down the commercial fields trimming the lower branches of the female plants to better encourage resin production, while at the same time eliminating the male plants. Indians believe the female plants yield much better ganja if they are not fertilized.

Cannabis lives from spring to fall, then dies. Next spring it reappears from the seeds that are unbelievably hardy. As long as the seeds can be protected by a soft covering of soil or leaves, cannabis will continue to spread as a wild weed. Under these conditions resin production tends to increase and its potency becomes much more marked. Cannabis does particularly well in areas where the soil is disturbed each year. Flooded plains provide an excellent medium for growth. Shady, stable areas will not permit the plant to reproduce itself, for cannabis thrives on soil instability. In general, it may be assumed that if thistle, milkweed, dandelion, and similar weed growths do well, cannabis will do even better.

Those interested in cultivating cannabis for industrial purposes are more concerned with plants grown in cold or temperate regions where the subsoil is moist and the rain is abundant. Plants growing in these areas are soft and fibrous and thus of greater commercial value. Hot, dry areas, on the other hand, produce brittle fibers and the resin produced in contrast to that occurring in plants grown in colder areas is copious, heavy, and sticky. The stickier the resin the greater the intoxication potential. Thus marijuana users prefer a plant grown under circumstances unfavorable to the best commercial hemp products.

The ubiquitous cannabis grows almost anywhere. It is a roadside flora in the southeastern United States; in the lowlands of the central United States countless acres are covered with clusters of the plant. It will grow in almost any sort of soil, even where the nutrition is quite poor. Those who wish to grow it purposefully may do so on rooftops, in backyards, and in other unorthodox places. Two recently came to light in widely separated parts of the country: in Glendora, California, police found two twenty-year-old users trying to grow their supply in a local cemetery; and in Detroit, Michigan, au-

4

thorities apprehended a known user trying to plant his garden in the center strip of the Willow Run Expressway! But the first prize for marijuana grown in obscure places goes to the variety noted by the *Marijuana Newsletter*[1] as "Manhattan Silver." It originated from seeds flushed down the sewer by frightened users who were suddenly raided by the police. Once the seeds hit the sewer they began to germinate, and, since they grew without sunlight, they produced a plant that was silver or white rather than green. Those in the know state that it was unusually potent.

Cannabis is so hardy and ubiquitous that anyone who wishes a supply of his own for tripping purposes faces little difficulty in securing it, other than having to guard against arrest. As John Rosevear,[2] who has written a step-by-step commentary describing the natural and artificial culture of the weed, has noted, "There are as many ways of growing marijuana as there are of growing corn." The Mexicans, for instance, merely poke a hole in the ground, dump in some seed and wait for nature to take over. The seeds are so easy to grow that if a handful is tossed on the ground and pressed in with one's foot they will usually anchor and become plants. There is little to hinder its growth since cannabis has few natural enemies.

If insects are reticent to pollenate cannabis, they are even less prone to consume it for food. Thus cannabis is almost immune to attacks by locusts, grasshoppers, and similar pests. As for spiders, they may build their nests around the base of the plant but they will not attack the plant itself.

Cannabis is unusually resistant to weather change, although heavy frosts may kill it. It can also be choked out by heavy vines and other strong weeds. The only significant enemy the weed really has is man, who has made various efforts to destroy it. But this is an uneven battle, for cannabis can reproduce itself and grow faster than man can detect and uproot it. The reproductive process is so insistent and so hardy that very few requirements are necessary for its survival. Rosevear notes this when he gives explicit instructions on cannabis cultivation, whether in a hothouse or in natural field gardens. Cannabis, he assures his readers, really takes care of itself once it has been given the chance to root. All one needs are minimal instructions for gardening, a little sun-light, water, tinfoil, earth, and one seed. "God," Rosevear intones, "will do the rest."[3]

RECOGNIZING CANNABIS

Once a person has seen the cannabis plant or smelled its resin or burning leaves, it is difficult to forget it. Cannabis even looks unusual. Its stalk is hollow, leafy, and four-cornered. It can become quite tall and may attain a height of some twenty feet. If uncrowded it will bush out with many branches. This is a disadvantage for one who wants to grow the plant for industrial purposes, since its fiber content is less if it grows uncrowded. It is an advantage to resin users, however, since sparse planting will increase the resin content. Cannabis smokers, therefore, try to keep their growing plants thinned down. Commercial producers, on the other hand, crowd them together.

The seeds are usually sown in May. The plants are harvested in September. When cannabis is full-grown its stalk may become three to four inches thick. Four ridges run lengthwise up this stalk with well-marked nodes or knots growing on it at four- to twenty-inch intervals. One of the more distinctive features of cannabis, if indeed the whole plant is not distinctive, is the appearance of its leaves. These are compound and consist of a number of smaller leaflets or lobules. The lobules are uneven in number, five to eleven being present in a single leaf. They are pointed at both ends like a slender canoe and are from two to six inches in length. The two outer leaflets are always smaller than the rest of the grouping. The sides of the leaflets are serrated (sawtoothed) and pronounced ridges run diagonally from their center to the edges. The upper side of the leaflet is dark green, its underside being a lighter green. Long hairs run along the bottom of the leaflets; these couple back or reach out and retract toward the underside.

If the plant has a heavy resin content it is sticky to the touch. Cannabis that grows in a hot, dry climate such as that of North Africa will produce so much resin that at noon, when the sun is hot, resin accumulates on the leaves in such concentration that the plant appears to be covered with dew. Cannabis also has a distinctive odor which, obviously, smells like a freshly made hemp rope. The bigger and greener the plant becomes, the more potent its resin will be.

The roots and branch roots of the plant are quite diversified. Usually one finds a long taproot that is about one-tenth as long as the stalk growing above the ground. From this root small branch roots spread out to anchor the plant firmly in the earth. When cannabis flowers, the blossom appears as an irregular cluster of light yellowish-green seeds. These egg-shaped seeds have encircling ridges with motley, lacy markings on their surfaces. On close examination they seem to be almost identical.

The plant retains its green color for long periods of time after it is cut. It may become somewhat brownish as it ages but only the very uninformed would mistake it for tobacco. When nonusers come into contact with cannabis it is either because someone shows it to them or because they inadvertently run across a supply, or "stash." When so encountered the weed will appear as a mound of semi-moist or partially dried leafy plants usually bunched together in a plastic bag. In this condition it is nondescript and may resemble any cut, semi-dried stored weed. Cannabis, however, has some differentiating features. It does not lose its moisture content fully for a long time, particularly if it is kept wrapped in plastic. It has a weedy, almost alfalfa-like odor especially when it is lit. When ignited it burns very hot and is easily extinguished. The odor of the burning plant is very sweet and distinctive. To smell it once is to remember it. Additionally, if one searches the bag of weed carefully, he will almost always find seeds; little brownish-yellow hard seeds with definite ridges along the sides.

One thing can be said about the bushy, green cannabis plant: it is quite ornamental. A surprising number of innocent gardeners have been called to task by observant narcotics officers who wanted to know why they were growing contraband substance in their yard. Occasionally this happening

7

strikes close to home. The author recalls one instance when his commanding officer at a U.S. Air Force base was descended upon by alert agents who inquired as to why he was fostering a sixty-foot hedge of marijuana across the front of his lawn!

WEED INTO GRASS

It's not the plant cannabis that causes all the current controversy: it's the resin of the thing. For in cannabis resin one finds potent psychotoxins. This group of psychotoxins is officially known as the cannabinols. Of these, none is more potent than the tetrahydrocannabinols (THC). There are many forms of THC; at least eighty derivatives have been synthesized and studied pharmacologically. In time scientists may find even more.

The principal synthetic forms of tetrahydrocannabinol appeared in the 1940's under the trade names synhexyl, pyrahexyl, and parahexyl. Their appearance marked the culmination of years of study of the complex chemistry of the active principals of cannabis. This chemistry remained a total mystery until 1942 when H. J. Wollner[4] and his co-workers first isolated and identified a natural tetrahydrocannabinol. Even today scientists are not certain of the exact state or proportion of cannabinols in cannabis resin which precipitates the psychological effects in man. Currently a number of carefully directed laboratory studies are under way to explore this problem further. In time someone may finally solve this continuing pharmacological puzzle.

In the meantime, resin-laden cannabis leaves have become widely used and much discussed. So much so that an entire vocabulary has arisen to denote cannabis, especially among users. Most are simply synonyms for cannabis, but they are tremendously varied and not necessarily linguistically related to each other. For the most part the words are street terms whose derivations may never be traced. The Latin term *cannabis* had a Greek origin (kannabis) whereas the English word *hemp* is derived from Middle English *hemp*e and the earlier Old English form *henep* or *haenep*. Etymologically *hemp* and *cannabis* as words derive from the same obscure and unknown source, probably from the East. Marijuana (marahuana) may have arisen from the Mexican-Spanish *mariguana* or the

Portuguese *mariguango,* both of which mean "intoxicant." On the other hand, it may have come from the Mexican-Spanish slang *Marijuana* (Mary Jane) or *Maria y Juana* (Mary and Jane), or even earlier from the Aztec *Milan-a-Huan* which the early Spanish conquerors could not pronounce and so enunciated *maria-juana* instead.

When English-speaking peoples refer to cannabis they usually employ the term *marijuana.* In these countries this term indicates a preparation made from the flowering or fruiting tops of the cannabis plant (excluding the seeds and leaves when not accompanied by the tops) from which the resin has not been extracted. If one talks about the cannabis plant per se, however, he may be referring to any plant of the genus cannabis. If one talks about cannabis resin, he is referring to the separated resin, whether crude or purified, which is obtained from the cannabis plant.

While it is true that the use of the term cannabis is international, it is not true even among specialists that there is any agreement as to what one should call the plant or its products. The synonyms, excluding the street terms, are almost legion and vary from country to country. The Indians refer to cannabis as *charas, bhang, ganja,* or *hashish.* Mexicans call it *mota, moto, Mo-tul,* and *manteca.* In Central Africa it may be referred to as *Mbanzhe, mata, kwane,* or *dagga.* Each country seems to have its preferred term or terms to refer to the plant. This may seem confusing, but it is simple compared to the philological confusion American slang has made of this terminology. It would take a separate dictionary such as Schmidt's *Narcotics: Lingo and Lore*[5] to even begin to list all of the terms, but included one will find: Mary Jane, mary, tea, grass, weed, pot, hemp, hay, boo, charge, gage, and green; additionally from association, with hard-narcotic users, even the term shit, a term sometimes used for heroin, has been transferred to marijuana. On a more literary level, eulogistic terms, mostly from the Orient, have also been applied to cannabis. Included are: The Heavenly Guide, The Soother of Grief, Light Heart, Joy, The Rejoicer, The Poor Man's Heaven, Pills of Glory, and Fancy's Leaf. There are many others.

The term cannabis in this country may call forth images of the typical marijuana cigarette; however, it should be understood that distinct differences exist between certain types of preparations. This difference occurs primarily in both the source and the potency of the resin. In the United States, thanks primarily to the hippie movement and its colorful exploration of Indian lore, there are five primary terms in use which should be defined: bhang, ganja, charas, hashish, and marijuana. The first four of these refer specifically to Indian preparations of hemp; the fifth is of course of Mexican origin.

Bhang is an Indian smoking mixture that contains the cut tops of uncultivated female *Cannabis indica* plants. It has a low resin content and therefore is not particularly potent. *Ganja* consists of the cut tops, the resin being left intact, of a specially harvested grade of the female *Cannabis indica*. It is from this segment of the cannabis plant that smoking mixtures, beverages, and sweetmeats are made. The potency is considerably greater than that of bhang. *Charas* comes from the same special plants used in preparing ganja but differs in that it consists of pure, unadulterated resin obtained from the tops of the plant grown for ganja. Americans refer to charas as *hashish*. This is the most potent existing pure form of naturally occurring cannabis resin and is from five to six times stronger in its psychotoxic effect as the resin found in marijuana.

Marijuana is a Mexican-Spanish synonym for bhang. In the Americas and England it refers, as previously noted, to preparations made from the flowering tops and leaves of local cannabis plants, that is, *Cannabis americana* or *mexicana*. American user preference dictates that most marijuana be *Cannabis mexicana* since this variety is more potent than that grown in the United States.

EFFECTS OF CANNABIS USE

It is significant to note that the only pertinent effects caused by the intake of tetrahydrocannabinol on the body are those manifested on the central nervous system. The principal activity is directed toward that area of the brain that, by reason of providing logic, philosophical ability, and reasoning

10

powers, differentiates man from the lower animals. These psychological effects will be discussed later. For the present this discussion will center on some, but not all, of the physical effects. Others will be mentioned subsequently at the appropriate place.

Physically there seem to be few lasting ill effects directly related to the abuse of cannabis. During the time the user is on the drug, however, certain physiological changes do occur and are noticeable if one has the chance to observe the smoker at the peak of his intoxication. A few minutes after the smoke has been inhaled there is an increase in pulse rate and a rise in blood pressure. At first the user's metabolic rate increases and he often feels the need to urinate. Either during or shortly after the use of the cannabis the blood sugar level begins to fall and the user becomes extremely hungry for sweets. This factor explains why drive-ins and hamburger shops are favorite haunts of many cannabis habitués.

As time goes on the irritant effects of the smoke cause the mouth to become dry. The throat becomes so scratchy that coughing and clearing of the nasopharynx is commonplace. This irritation may continue long after the bout of smoking, particularly if the user repeats his inhalation of the smoke at frequent intervals. The effects of this irritant smoke are particularly striking in persons suffering from asthma and comparable diseases of the respiratory tract.

Three effects upon the eyes are of particular interest. Two of these have long been used by law enforcement officers as presumptive signs of cannabis intoxication. If the user becomes sufficiently high (and it often takes very little intoxicant to achieve this effect), his pupils usually dilate. Consequently, individuals who chronically use cannabis are fond of wearing sunglasses (tea shades) both to cut down the amount of light reaching their sensitive retinas and to make their pupils less obvious to police. They wear these sunglasses day or night, driving or walking, high, or off their drug, both as a status symbol and an optical aid. This, incidentally, causes them to become very obvious to the police. Smoking also causes the ciliary vessels of the eyes to dilate. Thus the white of the eye appears red.

11

A third problem related to eyesight is not as well known, although it was reported by Mohan and Sood[6] almost five years ago. It is assumed, and probably correctly, that the effects of cannabis intoxication begin within a few minutes after inhalation of the smoke. These effects last for about twelve hours, the period varying with the smoker, the toxicity of the source, and the amount of drug intake. In the case reported by Mohan these symptoms lasted almost six weeks. This case is significant because it shows it is possible for the physical effects on the eyes occurring from cannabis use to last for long periods.

The case in point is that of an eighteen-year-old who began to feel giddy and sleepy shortly after ingesting food that contained *Cannabis indica*. This giddiness persisted for several days. Soon he began to experience difficulty turning his eyes to the left. The problem increased in severity until after a week his eyes remained in a fixed stare toward the right. In order to look forward he had to compensate by turning his head to the left. During this period all of his eye muscle movements were absent. Although he recovered without any lasting ill effects, he was incapacitated for about six weeks.

The effects of cannabis use on vision, however, are not limited to the three conditions described above. Numerous authors have reported the occurrence of visual hallucinations that distract or tend to terrify the beholder if they are part of a so-called "bad trip." And some authors, this one included, have encountered users who have had near-fatal experiences while driving because they became engrossed with a light or sound to the point where they took their hands off the wheel (but not always their foot off the accelerator) to concentrate better on the color, movement, intensity or rhythmic flashing of the light.

Although various physical effects tend to appear in some users and not in others, it has been noted that many become nauseated and may vomit or have diarrhaea following the intake of cannabis. Additionally, although the effects on the brain are usually those of a relaxed, pleasant euphoria, some individuals who are unusually susceptible to the effects of the drug or who become highly intoxicated by it may develop a transient psychotic state.

In proper classification cannabis is a true hallucinogen that possesses elements of both stimulation and depression. It has a drug abuse pattern that includes psychological dependence, some tolerance, and certain side effects, some of which have been previously mentioned. It is not pharmacologically a narcotic, although most state legislatures have chosen to declare it should be handled under the same laws as those that regulate narcotics. However, cannabis does not cause addiction in the proper sense of the word since addiction per se involves psychological dependence, tolerance, and physical dependence with the appearance of withdrawal symptoms if the drug is abruptly withdrawn from a chronic user with a sufficiently demanding habit.

Much has been said of the importance of physical addiction and the withdrawal syndrome when drug abuse is discussed. This is somewhat misleading, since physical addiction is one of the least important of the triad of requirements in the definition of an addicting drug. The single feature which is of vital importance in the abuse of any drug is the creation of psychological dependence. There is no question that the appearance of withdrawal symptoms will cause an addicted individual to return to the use of his drug to prevent physical discomfort, but it is the psychological dependence that makes him return again and again to the abuse of the drug of his choice even though physical dependence has been eliminated by withdrawal and discomfort is no longer a feature. Even drugs that produce physical dependence such as heroin make their chief claim upon users through psychological rather than physical dependence. This is revealed by the relative ease of withdrawal from narcotics by those who, for medical reasons, have become physically but not psychologically dependent upon drugs given for the control of pain.

The problem of classification in terms of addicting drugs tends to cloud the issue of present-day cannabis use. A solution to this semantic problem has recently been offered by the World Health Organization,[7] which suggested that a new nomenclature be devised to describe and categorize drugs. This organization suggested the terms *addiction* and *habituation* be replaced by the term "drug dependence" with accompanying features being considered a part of the total abuse syndrome. This nomenclature would make it easier and more accurate to speak of each drug in a manner that would leave no question as to its associated problems of use and abuse. One might, then, speak of the *cannabis dependence syndrome,* the *heroin dependence syndrome,* or for that matter, the *caffeine, nicotine,* or *alcohol dependence syndrome.* Perhaps someday this usage may be placed in effect.

CANNABIS AND MEDICINE

Throughout the centuries cannabis has been tried for almost every conceivable ailment. In some instances it did no harm; in others it was quite detrimental. In American medicine the fluid extract of cannabis has been used on occasion because some doctors felt it had a sedative or local analgesic effect. Today, it is no longer considered to be a valid therapeutic drug. The American Medical Association's Committee on Alcoholism and Drug Dependence[5] supported this judgment with the recent statement: "Cannabis (marihuana) has no known use in medical practice in most countries of the world, including the United States."

Such is cannabis: a weed, a commercial product, a sometimes medicinal drug, a psychotoxin. Its wild growth is determined by the capricious wind. It is cultivated by Indian ganja doctors, American hippies, and commercial manufacturers. Although American use of cannabis resin products is a recent phenomenon, the history of cannabis abuse is an old story in other parts of the world. Let us consider the history of the weed as a mind-expanding drug to understand better what cannabis has meant in the past to other societies and other peoples.

1. *Marijuana Newsletter,* quoted in John Rosevear, *Pot: A Handbook of Marijuana* (New York: University Books, 1967), p. 42.

2. *Ibid.,* p. 44.

3. *Ibid.,* p. 46.

4. H. J. Wollner, J. R. Matchett, and S. Loewe, "Isolation of a

14

physiologically active tetrahydrocannabinol from cannabis sativa resin," *J. Amer. Chem. Soc.,* 64:26-29 (1942).

5. J. E. Schmidt, *Narcotics: Lingo and Lore* (Springfield, Ill.: C. C Thomas, 1959).

6. H. Mohan and G. C. Sood, "Conjugate deviation of the eyes following cannabis indica intoxication," *Brit. J. of Opth.,* 48:160-161 (March, 1964).

7. "World Health Organization Expert Committee on Addiction-producing Drugs, Thirteenth Report," *Bull. Narc.,* 16(2):53-55 (April-June, 1964).

8. Council on Mental Health and Committee on Alcoholism and Drug Dependence, "Dependence on cannabis (marijuana)," *J.A.M.A.,* 201:368-371 (Aug. 7, 1967).

"Peace pipe, my eye! Somebody here is smoking pot!"

THE HISTORY OF
THE WEED

*And God said, let the earth bring
forth grass . . .*
—Genesis I:11

No one knows where it came from or, for that matter,
when man first discovered it, but cannabis was probably
known from the earliest of times. Even so, cannabis remains
almost as much of a puzzle today as it was when man first
discovered he could use it to heighten perception and distort
his concept of time, or as modern users say to "trip" or "turn
on." Considering the importance cannabis has played in the
socioeconomic history of the world, the lack of information
on the history of cannabis itself seems surprising. But, then,
cannabis is a surprising drug that can make the impossible
seem real and the real seem unnecessary.

How old is pot? Ask the hippie and he will tell you "grass"
is as old as Eden. He may even refer you to Genesis I:11
(quoted above) to substantiate his contentions. For to the hippie, the weed is a sacrament in a new religion that has arisen
from a trinity of love, nonconformity, and antimaterialism.
Hippies, however, do not quote from Genesis a comment
made by God some sixty-two verses later, when he dispatched
Adam and Eve from their paradise: "Cursed is the ground for
thy sake," He said, "In sorrow shalt thou eat of it all the days
of thy life; thorns also and thistles shall it bring forth to thee;
and thou shalt eat of the herb of the field." Cannabis, anyone?

In some ways cannabis has been beneficial to man. In earlier days many used the hemp plant as a source of rope, clothing, and to treat—usually with poor success—every imagin-
able illness. The full history of cannabis, then, is its history as
a commercial product, hemp, and as a psychotoxin. It is, of

course, in this second category that cannabis interests us today, and it is cannabis the psychotoxin that forms the subject of this chapter.

THE MYSTERIOUS ORIENT

History had to wait until the Chinese recorded the first adequate description of the hemp plant. Their writings indicate cannabis originated somewhere to the north of the Himalayan Mountains; but how it got there, or why, no one seems to know. The learned emperor Shen-Nung,[1] a surprisingly adept pharmacologist, was well aware of the effects of cannabis. About the year 2737 B.C. when he wrote his book on pharmacology he noted a number of still accurate observations concerning the hemp plant.

For centuries hemp remained the principal source of clothing for the Chinese, for this civilization failed to discover the practicality of using flax fiber. Why this is so is unknown. Perhaps, since they began with the hemp fiber and were satisfied with its product, they felt no need to develop an alternative. In any event, hemp was so commonly utilized that it was described in the Chinese treatise *Rh-Ya,*[2] compiled during the fifteenth century B.C. This work noted that hemp grew in both male and female forms and referred to it as *Ma,* a term that still has some colloquial usage.

During this period the Chinese developed an interesting folk custom. They took the hard hemp stalk and carved one end into the shape of a snake's head. When a Chinese became ill his friends or relatives would beat his bed with this "magic" totem, believing it had the power to dispel evil spirits. While the Chinese attributed supernatural powers to the hemp plant, they had little, if any, use for the peculiar resinous exudate that oozed from the flower clusters on the female plant. Contemporary Chinese moralists, watching the effects produced by the use of this resin in those wild youth of the era, concluded that this frenetic euphoria had no place in stable Chinese culture. Shortly, with proper warning to recalcitrant youths, the drug was labeled the "Liberator of Sin," and the use of the hemp plant or its resin as an escapist phenomenon forbidden to the Chinese.

Shen-Nung, however, was not opposed to utilizing cannabis in medicinal treatment. He prescribed it for beriberi, constipation, female weakness, gout, malaria, rheumatism, and, of
all things, absent-mindedness! One particularly interesting medicinal use of hemp resin was recorded about 220 A.D. in the
biography of the Chinese physician Hoa-Tho.[3] He mixed the
resin with wine, termed it *Ma-Yo,* and employed it as an anesthetic for controlling pain during various surgical procedures.
According to this ancient doctor one good dose and the patient was ready for the operating table. It was so effective that
later when he questioned his patients they all claimed they
were free of pain during their surgery.

It is an interesting commentary on the variance of psychological response produced by the use of cannabis when employed by different civilizations that the placid Chinese for the
most part did not appreciate its euphoria. Tranquil, smooth,
languorous reveries from opium, yes. Technicolor fantasies
from hemp exudate, absolutely no. The unpredictable reactions of hemp intoxication, sometimes stimulative, sometimes
sedative, seemed alien to the nature of this culture, which preferred, when it chose to relax, to utilize a predictable drug
that would afford it the chance to sleep and dream. Where
the ecstatic sensations and vivid hallucinations produced by
the use of hemp were concerned, however, the Chinese were
content to leave these to cultures more temperamentally suited
to enjoy them.

THE SONG OF MOTHER INDIA

South and west of the Chinese lived a people who could
more than appreciate the effects of hemp intoxication. The
land was India; its religion, significantly, Hinduism. Cannabis
was not indigenous to this area. More than likely it was taken
there from somewhere in central Asia, perhaps by Iranian
tribes. In the beginning hemp use was concentrated among the
more contemplative members of Indian society who desired its
effects to lessen the temptations and the noise of the external
world. This group used the drug to place worshippers in an
attitude of reverence by separating them from gross reality. In
a short time, however, cannabis use became widespread. When

19

it did, it became integrated into both the daily life and the religious activity of the people.

Unlike the Chinese, who cultivated hemp for its fiber and who forbade its aberrant pharmacological use, the people of India specifically employed the resin of the plant for its psychotoxic effect. Indeed, India perfected the use of cannabis for this purpose. Here, hemp culture became an agricultural science and its use an almost universal habit. For centuries, until recently when a governmentally sponsored program was begun to phase out the use of cannabis, nearly every system of Indian philosophy and religion was inextricably entwined with the use of Indian hemp.

The Indians looked upon their hemp plant with eyes that teared with love. They nearly deified the drug products of the plant and they developed a vocabulary for each type: bhang, charas, hashish, and ganja. Native literature extolled cannabis and called it holy. "A guardian" an Indian philosopher wrote "lives in the bhang leaf. . . . To see in a dream the leaves, plant, or water of bhang is lucky. . . . A longing for bhang foretells happiness. It cures dysentery and sunstroke, clears phlegm, quickens digestion, sharpens appetite, makes the tongue of the lisper plain, freshens the intellect and gives alertness to the body and gaiety to the mind. Such are the useful and needful ends for which in His goodness the Almighty made bhang. . . ."

The thought that someone might later come along and deprive the people of this magnificent experience caused these native writers to predict terrible consequences that could follow such deprivation: "To forbid or even seriously restrict so holy and gracious an herb as the hemp would cause widespread suffering and annoyance and to large bands of worshipped ascetics deep-seated anger. It would rob the people of a solace in discomfort, of a cure in sickness, of a guardian whose gracious protection saves them from the attacks of evil influences. . . ." Surprisingly, this Indian writer concluded his eulogy of cannabis with an apology: "So grand a result, so tiny a sin."[4]

Cannabis users had good reason to fear their ecstatic state might be interrupted. Disapproval soon was expressed by

Christian missionaries and other representatives of European culture who felt the use of the drug kept the people from being converted to Christianity. J. Campbell Oman, in his study of Indian mystics commented: "It would be an interesting philosophical study to endeavor to trace the influence of these powerful narcotics [charas and bhang] on the minds and bodies of the itinerant monks who habitually use them. We may be sure that these hemp drugs, known since very early times in the East, are not irresponsible for some of its wild dreaming." Oman also noted that Christian missionaries were inclined to remark sarcastically: "A great number of Hindu saints live in a state of perpetual intoxication and call this stupefaction, which arises from smoking intoxicating herbs, fixing the mind on God."[5]

The barrage of insults and protests from antagonistic bhang users failed to dent the enthusiasm of the masses, however, and they continued to make cannabis a part of their everyday lives. Despite growing pressure to eliminate cannabis use, it soon became known about the country as the "Happy Plant." Although the Indians were inclined to be preoccupied with euphoric effects and contemplative aid offered by the use of cannabis, they were not unaware of some of its other potentialities. The *Susruta*[6] compiled sometime before 1000 B.C., not only mentioned the euphoria-producing capability of hemp but also recommended its application for various diseases.

From the writing of the *Susruta* on, cannabis became increasingly mentioned in Indian literature. Some of these references contained dry humor. About the year 1500 A.D.[7] a story was transcribed concerning two rogues who were disturbing the peace by arguing over one of the "nymphs of the bazaar." At their trial the judge demanded they post bail. Complying, one of the defendants left his ganja bag as security. The judge not only accepted the offer but as soon as the defendants were out of sight he used the ganja for his own enjoyment. Thus, in Indian literature and in song, cannabis was extravagantly lauded, and soon, yogis, ascetics, and heroes were reported to rely on its support prior to performing important feats.

21

Eventually the club of cannabis users began equating themselves with the gods. "No god or man," native writers eulogized,[8] "is as good as the religious drinker of bhang." Accepting this philosophy, the Indian people more and more incorporated the use of the drug as an integral part of their religious worship. Theology students were given bhang prior to studying the scriptures. Holy men at sacred places took it prior to centering their thoughts on eternity. Ascetics employed it to enable them to go days without food or water. For those caught in the euphoric grasp of hemp, the drug seemed to provide the answer to all problems. To the Indian, unlike the Chinese who had rejected it, bhang offered a much desired experience. As opium had found its position in the life of the Chinese who wished to escape serenely the pressures of reality, bhang became a staple in the emotional experience of the introspective Indian.

The use of the drug, however, was not without complications. Soon cannabis became so important to those dependent on its effects that legislators became fearful of the ultimate result. Despite these fears the government, after a careful study that revealed the use of the drug was so widespread attempts at its elimination seemed almost futile, begrudgingly issued a recommendation to the League of Nations in 1930 to the effect that it was neither practical nor advisable to attempt to exterminate the practice.[9] Some thirty years later the government had to come to grips with this problem again. This time it legislated against the use of cannabis. In so doing, the Indian government appears to have accepted the argument that cannabis use has deleterious social consequences and to have embraced the position, maintained by diverse investigators that continued use of hallucinogenic drugs tends to eliminate the learned patterns of culture. So grand a result, so tiny a sin?

CANNABIS IN CLASSICAL ANTIQUITY

It was inevitable that once the knowledge of the effects of cannabis became known to the great nations of India and China, it would soon become known to other nations. West of India, in nearby Assyria, scholars were aware of a fascinating

22

plant they referred to in 650 B.C. as *Azallu*. This plant could not only be used in spinning and in rope-making but also to dispel depression of the spirit. Cannabis had reached the Middle and Near East.

About the same time the Homeric poems told of a drug that eliminated all pain and anger. It was so effective that Helen, daughter of Zeus, was said to have used it to lull her anguish and sorrow. So powerful was the drug, the poet rhapsodized, that if one used it he would not feel sorrow even though his mother and father died, nor cry if he saw his brother or dear son slaughtered before him.[10]

Herodotus[11] reported during this period that the Scythians were growing a plant that was thicker and taller than flax and produced a seed that, when thrown on red-hot stones in an enclosed space, was believed to cleanse the body. This activity produced a steam which, he noted, was so remarkable that Grecian vapor baths could not surpass it. Once the Scythians were transported with this vapor, they would shout and scream in frenzy. Herodotus also remarked about a group of people living along the Araxes River who met together in groups, made a fire and threw a weed into the flames. "By inhaling the burning food that has been thrown on," he said, "they become intoxicated by the odor just as the Greeks do by wine; and the more food that is thrown on, the more intoxicated they become until they rise up to dance and betake themselves to singing." This same technique, interestingly, was described by Burton[12] as a method employed by African savages in the late nineteenth century.

The classical world offers other commentary on the use of hemp. Pliny,[13] in the first century A.D., quotes the description of Democritus' concerning the use of a plant, "Potamaugis." This plant was probably hemp. Partaking of this plant produced a delirium. When it was taken internally with myrrh and wine it caused "all sorts of visionary forms" and precipitated "outbreaks of the most immoderate laughter." A few years later Dioscorides[14] accurately described and illustrated the hemp plant, commenting about its use in rope manufacturing and its curative power in cases of earache, edema, and assorted ills. Oddly, he failed to indicate it had any specific narcotic or intoxicating properties. A century later the great physician Galen[15] reported the use of cannabis as a confectionery dessert which, when taken after meals with drinks, caused exciting pleasure, created much warmth and, if overindulged in, affected the head. He recommended its use for extinguishing flatus, curing earache, and other problems.

CANNABIS IN ARABIAN COUNTRIES

As time progressed, the use of hemp products increased, and the problem of its abuse spread from place to place. It is improbable, however, that the plant was generally abused by the majority of the people who lived during the centuries just before and after the beginning of the Christian era, by which time it was well known in the eastern Mediterranean. More probably, as Walton[16] suggests, it was a folk custom practiced sporadically by various tribes in isolated localities. By 500 A.D. cannabis was being used throughout most of Europe except for the far west. Arabic physicians employed the drug for numerous ailments, including its administration as an aphrodisiac. About 950 A.D. an Arabian physician noted that the hemp that was used for rope-making could ease headaches. Concurrently, other Arabian writers complained that hashish drugs were enjoying too great a popularity, so much so that stories about the joyful effects of the drug had come to occupy a prominent place in Arabian literature. *The Tales of the Arabian Nights* recounted lurid stories of the effects of hashish abuse. Undoubtedly these tales led more young Arabs to try the drug.

One of the early Arabian manuscripts relates the story of a Moslem priest who stood in the mosque exhorting his listeners to avoid the use of "beng" because it intoxicated the user and produced sleep. Soon he was transported by his harrangue and began flailing his arms about to emphasize his point. This caused his robe to loosen. As it did, the priest's private source of beng, which he had wrapped in paper and tucked away in his gown, fell to the ground where his listeners could see it. Instead of losing his cool, the priest seized upon this unanticipated object lesson to strengthen his argument. "This is the enemy," he cried, "this demon of which I have told you; the

24

force of my words has put it to flight; take care that in quitting me it does not hurl itself on one of you and possess you." Cowed by this outburst, no one in the audience dared to touch the paper full of beng. To be certain, however, the priest stood guard to protect his property. As soon as the crowd dispersed, the priest recovered his precious package and retired to enjoy himself. He fooled, the translator noted, no one but himself.[17]

By the middle of the thirteenth century A.D., adverse conditions arose for Arabian hashish users. In 1251 the Garden of Cafour, near Cairo, notorious for the abuse of hashish by its fakirs, was destroyed. This destruction was viewed by contemporary writers as a "just punishment of God." These men also complained about the existence of another small colony in the Canton of Timbaliere. Here hashish was not only sold, its use by the inhabitants of the colony was almost universal. The drug was employed in Timbaliere, said the critics, by the most degenerate of people, libertines, and feebleminded individuals, who vied with each other to see who could outdo the other in use of the drug. This they did without shame, one scribe observed; yet it was not always so, "for I have seen myself a time," he noted, "in which it [cannabis] was regarded as the vilest of filth and most revolting excrement."[18]

While denouncing the behavior of the hashish abusers, this social philosopher expressed even more concern about the ultimate effects of the use of the drug on people who might be tempted to abuse it in the future. "In truth," he said, "there is nothing which is more dangerous to the temperament. As it is known today by everybody in Egypt, in Syria, in the Irak and in the country of Roum, we believe we should speak of it in some detail." And speak they did. But to no avail, for the drug habit had caught the fancy of many who would not relinquish it.

The most revealing story of drug use in Arabia concerns the utilization of cannabis by a character known as Hasan-Ibn-Sabbah who, to the joy of most of his contemporaries, finally died in 1124 A.D. Sometimes called the "Old Man of the Mountain" (a term originally applied to one of Hasan's followers, Rachid-al-Din Sinan by the Crusaders who feared

25

him) Hasan was a vigorously ambitious, fanatical, vicious, religious kook. He was also a well-educated, well-familied (he claimed to be a descendant of the Himyarite kings of South Arabia) cruel, disciplined, ruthless, anti-Christian.

Educated in his youth in Egypt, Hasan returned to his native land as a Fatimid missionary. He soon abandoned his religious philosophy, organized a secret cult based on Ismailite antecedents and developed an agnostic philosophy that was dedicated to overthrowing previous doctrines and encouraged his young followers to believe nothing and dare all.

Hasan acquired a strong mountain fortress, the Alamut (eagle's nest) northwest of Qazwin in 1090 A.D. From there he began a series of surprise raids that netted him other fortresses and enlarged his following. He organized his army well and taught them to use the dagger as it had never been used before. In short, he refined the practice of assassination to an art. Using this art of political murder, which was thereafter to bear his name, Hasan plunged the Muslim world into terror by murdering his erstwhile friend the vizier, Nizam-al-Mulk, in 1092 A.D. The murder was carried out by a drugged hatchet man, all of which brings us to the point of our story.

Although Hasan had an elaborate system of command with a caste system of officers at his behest the dirty work was carried out by young men in their late teens and early twenties called Fidawi (or fida'is). These young men were recruited, plied with luxuries and sworn to total allegience to Hasan. Philip Hitti,[19] quoting from the *Book of Ser Marco Polo*, relates the impressions Marco Polo acquired of the assassin situation when he passed through Hasan's area in 1271 A.D. or thereabouts. Polo describes a marvelous garden that Hasan had constructed at the Alamut for the entertainment of his young assassins, noting that no one was permitted entry to this garden area except those who were pledged to die at Hasan's command.

> There was a fortress at the entrance to the Garden strong enough to resist all the world, and there was no other way to get in. He (Hasan) kept at his Court a number of the youths of the country, from twelve to twenty years of age,

such as had a taste for soldiering. . . . Then he would introduce them into his Garden, some four, or six, or ten at a time, having first made them drink a certain potion which cast them into a deep sleep, and then causing them to be lifted and carried in. So when they awoke they found themselves in the Garden.

When therefore they awoke, and found themselves in a place so charming, they deemed that it was Paradise in very truth. And the ladies and damsels dallied with them to their hearts' content. . . . So when the Old Man would have any prince slain, he would say to such a youth: "Go thou and slay So and So; and when thou returnest my Angels shall bear thee into Paradise. And shouldst thou die, natheless even so will I send my Angels to carry thee back into Paradise."

The remarkable ingredient Hasan used to lower the inhibitions of these young men and make them susceptible to his lies and delusions was the resin of the hemp plant. The resin worked so well, as Gautier[20] has described it, that, "Those taking it, on awaking from their intoxication, found real life so sad and colorless that they joyfully sacrificed it to re-enter the paradise of their dreams; for every man who was killed while accomplishing the order of the sheik went straight to heaven, while those who escaped were again permitted to enjoy the felicities of the mysterious concoction."

Hasan's story has been told many times since the days of Marco Polo. Probably the most popular version is that in Alexandre Dumas' book *The Count of Monte Christo*. Philologists dispute whether the word *assassin* derives from *Hasan* or from *hashish;* some maintain that *hashish* itself derives from *Hasan*. One thing is certain, however; *Hasan, hashish,* and *assassin* were all tied up together in the days when the Fidawi were strewing corpses across the Moslem crescent. And the combination of disturbed personalities and a dangerous drug resulted in the same outcome then as it does today, though now the situation seems less romantic.

The descendants of Hasan live with us still. They are scattered sparsely through northern Syria, Persia, Zanzibar, and in particular, India. They go now by the name of Thojas or Mowlas rather than Ismailites. They are led, not by a bloodthirsty assassin but instead by a gentle, well-educated young man who is interested in his people. His followers respond by tithing their income to provide him with financial support, a factor that makes the ruler independently wealthy. Though he claims direct descent from the terrifying grand master of Alamut his interests are much different. His followers revere him as the seventh imam. Americans know him better as the Aga Khan.

THE DRUG ARRIVES IN AFRICA

About the thirteenth century the central Africans discovered the intoxicating experience afforded by breathing hemp vapors. Their technique was simple: they threw the weed on the fire, then stood around inhaling the smoke. Soon they became more sophisticated. Prostrating themselves on the ground, they poked hollow tubes toward the hot embers to acquire the smoke more directly. Later they elevated these fires to the tops of tall stumps so they could sit or stand while smoking. African Bushmen discovered they could modify the irritating effects of hemp smoke if they took a mouthful of water before they inhaled. In time even this technique was improved upon, and smokers used a hollow antelope horn partially filled with water and with the burning hemp placed on the larger open end. The smoke could then be "drunk."

Over the following centuries practices in cannabis use were modified and changed as the hemp habit traveled through various tribes. The habit remained new to some and unknown to others, however, a fact supported by Livingstone's comments[21] in the mid-nineteenth century that, while younger men of the upper Zambezi River tribes smoked cannabis, the older men were often unaware of its effects. Eventually, crude pipes were developed to improve the effects of smoking hemp. The gourd, the coconut, and bamboo stems were employed to achieve the best effect. Finally, pottery-makers in North Africa stumbled upon the idea of making a water pipe to cool the smoke and remove some of its irritants. The hashish pipe thus came into being. This is still the most common means of cannabis consumption for the "kif" smokers of North Africa.

In Egypt cannabis use increased from the thirteenth century on. Eventually officials began to make desperate, albeit unsuccessful, attempt to eradicate it. By 1789, when Napoleon began his invasion of Egypt as a preliminary toward the conquest of British India, hashish abuse was so prevalent among Egyptian lower classes that the French legislated severe penalties for the sale or use of the drug. Napoleon was zealous in his attempts to eliminate Egyptian hashish dens, but his attempts were less than successful. He discovered, as have others before and after him, that once the cannabis camel enters the tent it is extremely difficult to get him to move out again. The situation Napoleon found in Egypt continues to this day and, according to recent press reports, the habitual use of marijuana in Egypt has reached alarming levels. In 1960 the Egyptian government issued the following statement on cannabis:

> . . . the prepared product of [the] cannabis sativa plant, while having very little useful medical use, is capable of profoundly disturbing the brain cells and inducing acts of violence, even murder; that it is in fact a fairly vicious and dangerous thing of no value whatever to humanity and deserving of nothing but the contempt of civilized people.

Recently these sentiments, published in 1960 by Goodman and Gilman,[22] were supported by Masters and Houston,[23] who note that the use of cannabis still accounts for a high percentage of Arab worker absenteeism and for a large percentage of the mental illness in Egypt. These authors state that in both Indian and Moslem cultures the social impact of the use of hemp has been enormous. This has equally been true of many African Negro cultures where the plant is worshipped and its use believed to bestow supernatural powers on the witch doctors. Cannabis appears to have contributed to some of the excesses in the recent Congo disorders. The followers of Patrice Lumumba were frequently intoxicated by hemp during battle. The shade of Hasan-Ibn-Sabbah continues to hang over much of Africa.

CANNABIS IN EUROPE

Except for areas bordering directly on the Mediterranean, Europe per se did not experience the cannabis abuse problem until recent years. In the middle of the last century in Europe a number of scientific investigators suggested that the products of the plant might have beneficial medical qualities. Oddly, for those scientists who dared to probe the secrets of the hemp plant, cannabis seemed to carry its own private curse. Easterfield and Spivey, the first pioneers to hydrogenate and nitrate cannabinol, one of the active ingredients in hemp resin, were soon killed in separate laboratory explosions. O'Shaughnessy, who pressed for a medical evaluation of the resin, was killed in an accident while investigating the drug.[24]

In 1844, in Paris, the famous Club des Hachichins was established at the swank Hotel Pimodan. The specialty of this club was a sweetmeat, Dawamesc, which contained hashish. This dish was introduced to the romantic society of the day from Algeria where it was frequently served as a delicacy. As a dessert it was eaten by many notables who came to the hotel to meet, eat, and become intoxicated by this strange drug.

Not all of those who frequented the club came to escape reality. Actually, interest in the drug which eventually spread throughout the Bohemian elements of Paris, began with an idea fostered by Dr. Jacques Moreau. Moreau was a respected physician at the Hospital de Bicetre, whose staff had initiated reform in the treatment of the mentally ill. Moreau believed cannabis could be used therapeutically to manage the emotionally disturbed. It was Moreau who introduced the use of the drug to the impressionable twenty-four-year-old popular author Théophile Gautier. Gautier, intrigued more with the bizarre emotional effect of the drug than with its medical potential, established the Pimodan Hotel hashish club. The doctor and the young author remained good friends, despite the variance of their interest in hashish; so much so that when Moreau published his findings in 1845 on the use of hashish in the treatment of the mentally ill he included a report by Gautier.[25]

Gautier, impressionable, artistic, creative, receptive, has given literature some of its most descriptive passages on the glories of hashish. A provocative author, Gautier began his literary career by writing a novel, *Mademoiselle de Maupin*, in which he described the adventures of a transvestite. Gautier had his own ideas concerning social value and expressed them vigorously in statements such as, "Enjoyment seems to me to be the end of life, and the only useful thing in the world."[26]

To Gautier and men like him, hashish offered a heady escape from the pressures of reality. But even with the influence of such eloquent advocates, the use of cannabis did not gain a significant foothold in western Europe until recent years. Then it was stimulated by American travelers and by the international press. As it has appeared in major cities of Europe officials have labeled it "the American vice," considering it another cultural offering to Europe from the United States.

WELCOME TO AMERICA

Cannabis was known and used in the New World as a euphoria-producing agent when Columbus was attempting to prove the world was round. During the early sixteenth century, and possibly before, it was utilized in certain Aztec religious ceremonies. Montezuma II was known to partake of a strange postprandial tobacco that caused him to fall into a deep sleep. It is possible that this strange tobacco was cannabis, although historians are not altogether certain.

In the late sixteenth century an English decision to increase Britain's shipping fleet made hemp cultivation a vital necessity, for flax could not provide the long, flexible, strong ropes needed for sea duty; nor could it be satisfactorily used for caulking as could hemp rope once it had served its original purpose. England compounded its hemp supply problems at this time by becoming embroiled in a series of disagreements with the Dutch. This automatically curtailed the British supply of hemp, which came largely from the Dutch East Indies. To remedy this, England decided to utilize its New World Colonies as a new hemp supply source. Thus, in 1611, near Jamestown, Virginia, cannabis was first purposely planted and grown in what is now known as the United States. Instructions were given the Colonists by His Majesty King James I, to increase hemp production. Apparently the Colonists made every effort to comply. By 1630 hemp became a staple of the colonial clothing industry. Soon half the Colonists' winter clothing and most of their summer clothing, were woven from its fibers.

A century later, however, in 1770, steam power began to replace the sail on ships. About the same time, Eli Whitney invented his cotton gin. With the demand for hemp markedly decreased, its cultivation was abandoned in America. The remaining plants were allowed to go to seed and return to weed status. Slowly, borne by the wind, this seed spread across the United States where it grew and regrew, waiting for the arrival of another generation who would find a use for it. It had to wait a long time—until the middle of our century.

Cannabis failed to enjoy any significant popularity as a euphoriant in the United States until Mexican laborers began to bring their little bags of "mota" across the border in the early part of this century. The first significant endemic use of the drug in this country began in New Orleans. Once the practice caught hold it spread quickly. By 1926 New Orleans was saturated with cannabis users. Since the weed grew with facility, the supply was more than adequate for a time. Soon, however, river sailors took the habit from New Orleans and spread it up the Mississippi River. Four years later small groups of marijuana smokers could be found in almost all major cities of the United States.

In the Thirties the demand for cannabis became so intense that Mexican laborers could not meet the market requirements. To forestall any shortage, shipments now began arriving from Havana, Tampico, and Vera Cruz. Marijuana importation became a full-time occupation with some, and the price jumped from an original ten dollars a kilo (2.2 pounds) to nearly fifty dollars.

By 1936 the government of the United States began to take a serious look at the increasing use of this drug. Unfortunately, irresponsible journalists became the loudest voices in this controversy and soon launched a series of myths which even today are used to argue against the use of marijuana. Whipped by yellow journalism, inflamed by ridiculous and untrue stories, the public panicked. A year later, 1937, the government passed the Federal Marijuana Tax in an attempt to control the distribution and thus the abuse of the drug.

These laws have had a significant effect in controlling the use of cannabis. They have also become the center of a great deal of controversy, a point that will be discussed later. Users of the drug now faced the alternative of quitting or going underground. For the most part the hard-core users followed the second course.

For quite a long time, as Rosevear[27] noted, cannabis was, as it still is, extremely popular among musicians, a large number of whom are Negro. Since the use of cannabis seems to mitigate the force of some of the problems facing certain Negroes, use of the drug by this group continued at a relatively high level, albeit clandestinely. Cannabis use was not and is not limited to this group by any means, but it did seem to offer this particular segment of society more than any other a much appreciated escape from the pressures of life.

With the coming of the civil rights movement and racial integration in the Fifties and the hippie movement in the Sixties, social forces mingled black with white, and users with nonusers. Cannabis use increased. Further, the spread of contemporary versions of the hedonist philosophy has encouraged many to experiment with a drug alleged to bring only pleasure and to have no ill effects. The use of cannabis by Mexican, Negro, and other minority groups in the first half of this century in the United States was a mere introduction to the story of cannabis in America. The first chapter is now being written as marijuana use spreads to a wider segment of society. Whether succeeding chapters will repeat the experiences of India, the Near East, and Africa or rather those of China and Europe depends upon who writes them. Where we stand today on the matter of *Cannabis sativa* will be the subject of the following pages.

1. Shen Nung, quoted in Norman Taylor, *Narcotics: Natures Dangerous Drugs* (New York: Dell Pub. Co., 1963), p. 11.

2. E. Bretschneider, "Botanicum sinicum: Mareria medica of the ancient Chinese," *J. North China Branch Shanghai Roy. Asiatic Soc.,* 25:66 (1890-91); 29:378 (1894-95). (Quoted in Robert P. Walton, *Marijuana: America's New Drug Problem* (Philadelphia: J. B. Lippincott 1938), p. 2.

3. S. Julian, "Substance anesthétique employée en Chine, dans

le commencement du III siècle de notre ère, pour paralyser momentanément la sensibilité." *Compt. Rend. Acad. Sci. Paris,* 28:195-198 (1894). (Quoted in Walton, *op. cit.,* p. 2.)

4. *Indian Hemp Drugs Commission Report* (Government Printing Office: 1893-94), 3:250. (Quoted in Walton, *op. cit.,* p. 5.)

5. J. Campbell Oman, *The Mystics: Ascetics and Saints of India* (London: T. F. Unwin, 1903). (Quoted in Walton, *op. cit.,* p. 5.)

6. R. N. Chopra, *Indigenous Drugs of India* (Calcutta: Art Press, 1933.) (Quoted in Walton, *op. cit.,* p. 3.)

7. *Indian Hemp Drugs Commission Report, op. cit.* (Quoted in Walton, *op. cit.,* p. 3.)

8. *Ibid.,* 3:250.

9. League of Nations, Geneva, 1928-30, Advisory Committee on Traffic in Opium and Dangerous Drugs, 1:12. (Quoted in Walton, *op. cit.,* p. 4.)

10. Homer, *The Odyssey,* Book IV, p. 220 (Chicago: Great Books of the Western World, Encyc. Brit. Inc., 1952).

11. Herodotus (English translation by Carey, 1848), IV, chaps. 74-75, and I, chap. 202. (Quoted in Walton, *op. cit.,* p. 8.)

12. R. F. Burton, trans., *The Book of the Thousand Nights and a Night.* (Benares: Kamashastra Society, 1885), X, 91. (Quoted in Walton, *op. cit.,* p. 8.)

13. Pliny, quoted in Walton, *op. cit.,* p. 8.

14. Dioscorides, Quoted in Walton, *op. cit.,* p. 8.

15. Caludius Galen, *Galeni Librorum* (Venice: 1597), De Alimentorum Facultatibus, Cap. 34, 15 F. Secunda Classis. (Quoted in Walton, *op. cit.,* p. 8.)

16. Walton, *op. cit.,* p. 10.

17. *Ibid.*

18. Sylvester DeSacy, *Chrestomathie Arabe* (1826), II, 138-143. (Quoted in Walton, *op. cit.,* p. 12.)

19. Philip K. Hitti, "The Assassins," in *The Book of Grass* edited by George Andrews (New York: Grove Press Inc., 1967), pp. 23-25.

20. Theophile Gautier (translated by Ralph J. Gladstone), "The Hashish Club," in *The Marijuana Papers,* edited by David Solomon (Indianapolis: Bobbs-Merrill, 1966), p. 124.

21. John Rosevear, *Pot: A Handbook of Marijuana* (New York: University Books, 1967), p. 73.

22. Louis S. Goodman, and Alfred Gilman, *The Pharmacological Basis of Therapeutics,* (2d ed.; New York: Macmillan, 1955), p. 174.

23. R. E. L. Masters, and J. Houston, *Varieties of Psychedelic Experience* (New York: Holt, Rinehart, and Winston, 1966), p. 37.

24. Rosevear, *op. cit.,* p. 146.

25. Jacques J. Moreau, "Du Hachich et de l'alienation mentale," quoted in *The Drug Experience,* edited by David Ebin (New York: The Orion Press, 1961), p. 4.

26. David Ebin, ed., *The Drug Experience, ibid.,* pp. 4-5.

27. Rosevear, *op. cit.,* p. 24.

"Gloria will be down in a minute. Would you like
some pot or something while you wait?"

THE WORLD OF MARIJUANA 3

> *"You know, when you don't turn on, you don't know anybody else who does. When you do, then it seems you don't know anybody else who doesn't."*
>
> —Mrs. Garnet Brennan
> (*Life*, Nov. 17, 1967)

A decade ago few people mentioned cannabis. Those who did whispered about it in the same hushed tones they reserved for discussions of sex and venereal disease. Those were the days when nobody had any use for marijuana. Usually they would not even discuss it. During that period the noted pharmacologists Goodman and Gilman described the contemporary cannabis user. He was, they said, "usually twenty to thirty years of age, idle and lacking in initiative, with a history of repeated frustrations and deprivations, sexually maladjusted (often homosexual), who seeks distraction, escape, and sometimes conviviality by smoking the drug. He almost uniformly has major personality defects and is often psychopathic."[1]

There was nothing wrong with this description then. There is nothing wrong with it even now *as it relates to this particular group of cannabis users*. These were the users who invariably progressed to heroin; these were the sociopaths who routinely flowed in and out of police stations; these were the so-called "dope fiends" who took that "incarnation of evil"— marijuana. And marijuana, according to posters of the day, caused mental deficiency, crime, physical deterioration, addiction, and anything else poster writers happened to think of. But no one cared. Cannabis use was essentially confined to a very limited group of citizens. Most teenagers had other ways of rebelling against their elders and flouting adult laws. Only the truly delinquent used marijuana.

37

This caricature of the cannabis user became deeply ingrained in the popular mind and still persists even though the user picture has drastically changed. It is so different that the current edition of the Goodman and Gilman text no longer contains the old description of the cannabis user. It just doesn't fit anymore. Today's users are, for the most part, well-educated middle- and upper-class young people. The sudden realization that this is so has caught society by surprise and created grand confusion. A survey of the marijuana scene today is therefore in order.

THE RANGE OF USE

Overnight, it seems, cannabis has become the "in" thing to use; and overnight two sharply divergent camps have been established in regard to the meaning of the marijuana revolution. Both camps have joined in playing a new game. It is called, says writer Jerry Cohen, "Expert Witness," and involves professors, doctors, ministers, criminologists, and so forth, who line up on opposite sides and joust among themselves while speaking knowledgeably about "grass," "joints," "roaches," and what have you.[2] These camps are so widely separated in viewpoint it is almost impossible for the authorities involved to sustain an intelligent debate. Pro-cannabis people are so certain the drug can serve as a cure-all for every cultural ill that they cannot see its potential for producing great social harm. The more these men talk to users who experience no apparent complications from cannabis use (or the more these men use it themselves), the more certain they are that the whole cannabis problem is a sham and that the drug should be legally, morally, and socially approved.

In the other corner, weighing in with an impressive number of authorities, both real and imagined, we find the anti-cannabis people. This group is so violently opposed to cannabis and so certain it is a diabolical underminer of everything holy they become apoplectic at any suggestion the drug might not be as bad as it has been previously painted. These men are as subjective in their own way as the pro-cannabis clan. Caught between these dissenting groups we find the rest of the citizenry, who by now are getting a little dizzy and disgusted, not to say a bit confused, as they listen to all the un-distilled verbiage that emanates from so many "authorities."

Just how common is cannabis use in America? Frankly, nobody knows. A few valid statistics indicate the extent of the local problems; by piecing these together we can try to estimate the national use. Even so, it is currently inaccurate to say that any given percentage is valid for the country as a whole. This much we do know: cannabis use by American youth, and even by many not-so-young people, is on the increase. Among American youth, cannabis is currently the major drug of abuse. But it may be losing its glamor. As "older children" hop onto the bandwagon (professors, doctors, theologians, and the like) it is getting to the point, as Dr. David Smith of Haight-Ashbury clinic fame has noted, that narcotics and hallucinogens may be losing some of their distinction as a young-adult hangup.[3]

Professionals on the sociological firing line who have to deal with the complications of cannabis abuse are almost obsessive in their determination to try to do something at least to keep the situation under control. This is particularly true of enforcement officers from the federal level on down. It is also true of organized medicine, which has had to take a stand through committee action on the cannabis situation. Most of these professionals have no axe to grind. The medical profession, for instance, cannot properly be accused, as police are often accused by the uninformed, of making a living by controlling the situation. The doctors' only interest is public health and safety. With some outstanding permissive exceptions, they present a solid front against the use of this drug. One representative expert is Dr. Nathan B. Eddy, who has spent forty years working on problems related to drug abuse for the National Academy of Sciences. He is wholeheartedly against legalizing the use of cannabis. "The only use for marijuana is to achieve gratification," Dr. Eddy says. "Society cares enough about having alcohol available to pay the immense social and economic cost of having millions of people depending on it. If we are thinking clearly we will not make freely available yet another agent of abuse and magnify the costs we pay."[4]

Such warnings, however, are watered down by those within

the profession, primarily those psychiatrists and sociologists who are well known for their permissive approach to life. These men repeatedly issue the glad tidings that "pot is here to stay," "pot is cool," "pot can't possibly hurt you." for the most part, the observations seem based on wishful thinking and a desire to give the people what they want despite the social cost.

One of the most vocal of the enthusiasts is a San Francisco psychiatrist who argues: "If marijuana were not called terrible by society, everyone would find that it is a mild drug that has little effect except to stimulate the appetite, slow down the time sense and create mild euphoria. It will not transform an individual into a monster." He further assures the nation's youth: "It doesn't cause crime and doesn't lead to the use of stronger drugs, sexual excess or deviant conduct—nor is it likely to cause mental illness or automobile accidents."[5] Such permissive counsel sows confusion and may ultimately contribute to the now large-scale problem of cannabis use in the United States.

Just how large is the problem? It is big enough so that at the nation's most prestigious educational institutions one can find cannabis with very little effort. A reasonably satisfactory estimate of its campus use, according to Gallup[22] is that some 22 percent of the college crowd has used marijuana at some time or another. Though statistics vary for adolescent use it may be reasonably assumed the use factor is about the same for teenagers.

In Great Neck, New York, where the average family income is $15,700 and where the school system is rated among the nation's ten best, a recent survey conducted by the two senior high schools in that city produced some eye-opening statistics. Of the 2,587 students polled, 207 (about 10%) said they had smoked cannabis. Many of these averred that they would do it again. Twenty-five percent of these students felt the drug should be legalized. In the same student body about fifty-five students (about 2%) said they had used LSD, DMT, or a comparable hallucinogen, and 12 percent said these drugs should be legalized too.[6]

A physician in charge of student health at the University of California at Berkeley recently testified that one out of four of the 27,000 students on his campus had smoked marijuana.

He "felt" that in some eastern universities, especially in urban areas, the use statistic might be as high as 60 percent. He also said that from 6 to 8 percent of the Berkeley campus students took LSD.[7]

In contrast to the Berkeley physician's opinion (which, to this author's knowledge, was unsubstantiated), those who hope their children go to school to learn and not to take cannabis may find encouragement in the objective findings of the Narcotics Subcommittee of the Medical Society of the County of New York.[8] Headed by competent Dr. Donald B. Louria, the committee was formed to take a close look at the drug abuse situation in New York City's ninety-five high schools and New York State's forty-eight colleges. The study was authorized because the society recognized that although many newsworthy statistics had been promulgated by cannabis enthusiasts and opponents alike over the past few months, very few if any of these "statistics" had been buttressed by factual data.

Although educational institutions are often lambasted for their apparent disinterest in problems relating to the abuse of drugs on their campuses, the schools and colleges of New York City and State responded admirably to this survey. Sixty-eight of the ninety-five New York City high schools (72% and forty-three of the forty-eight colleges (90%) returned the questionnaires concerning drug abuse on their campuses. Those familiar with studies of this sort will recognize this is an unusually high response.

The committee fully recognized the dangers of relying on statistics per se. For one thing, the committee realized this study revealed the hard-core or chronic user and not the occasional user who often escapes the attention of authorities. This, however, gives the final picture even more accuracy, since one cannot validly call a youngster who tries cannabis once and not again a "user" in the proper sense of the word. Moreover, the committee was cognizant that a communications gap is often present between student happenings and faculty awareness which could alter the figures to some extent. Finally, they knew the problem might be greater in nonreporting schools and that some administrators prefer not to face the truth or release accurate information if it is negative.

41

Despite these potential disadvantages, this report is significant because it represents a large and reasonably honest sampling recently carried out by competent authorities in an attempt to find out just what the user picture really is in that city. Because drug abuse is greater in New York City than in any other American city the findings are of national significance insofar as they tend to indicate a national trend.

Among responding New York City high schools, thirty-one of the sixty-eight reported no illicit use of drugs at all. Thirty-four of the thirty-seven which did report drug abuse said that less than 1 percent of the student body was involved. Of the remaining three schools, two reported between 1 and 10 percent of students illicitly using and one noted a 20 percent incidence of drug abuse. Thus of all reporting schools, only three had a significant drug abuse problem.

In six of the schools reporting drug abuse, marijuana abuse was the only problem. In nine others, barbiturates, with or without glue-sniffing, caused concern. In four others the abuse picture involved marijuana, glue-sniffing, and barbiturates. In two schools, glue-sniffing was the only drug abused. In three the data were unclear. In the remaining thirteen schools a mixture of drugs was used. Seven of these thirteen reported a total of eight cases of heroin use. In six, amphetamine abuse was the problem. In three of these six, amphetamine abuse constituted the major difficulty. Only one of the schools reported LSD usage. In each of the three schools with over 1 percent incidence of drug use, marijuana, amphetamines, and barbiturates were used, but not LSD or heroin. There were six reports of barbiturate overdosage, including two deaths due to an excessive intake of these drugs. An additional student died of narcotic overdosage.

In the colleges and universities, sixteen of the forty-three reporting said they had no drug problem. Seventeen others had a minor problem with less than 1 percent of the student body being involved. Of the other ten, eight noted an illicit drug use incidence of between 1 and 10 percent, one between 10 and 20 percent, and one of 40 percent. Of the twenty-six specifying the drugs abused, marijuana was the only or the predominating drug used on campus in fourteen colleges. In six others, amphetamines were the sole or predominating drug of abuse. In another four colleges amphetamines and barbiturates were in circulation. In the remaining two, hallucinogens were abused in one, whereas in the other college, a single student had become involved with heroin. Twelve of the forty-three colleges reported use of stronger hallucinogens, but it was a major problem in only one school. Of the ten colleges with what might be termed major problems, amphetamine abuse predominated in four and marijuana use in five. In one other institution marijuana, barbiturates, and amphetamines were used equally.

Several interesting points emerge from this study. In the high schools, marijuana, barbiturates, and glue were the drugs principally abused. In colleges, students preferred marijuana and amphetamines. Neither group used heroin or hallucinogens, such as LSD, with any frequency. While the committee emphasizes their report was not meant to minimize the drug abuse problem in their high schools and colleges, they did feel that the study supported the belief that most students are not interested in abusing drugs to any significant extent. They also noted that most of the students who did abuse drugs among the high school group were primarily dropouts who, the committee felt, should be controlled and supervised in their relationships with continuing students in order to prevent the spread of the drug abuse pattern.

Although this report is now almost two years old at the time of this writing, it remains significant because the study was performed near the top of the parabola of news releases that implied the abuse of cannabis was becoming a monstrous and overwhelming problem. The fact of the matter, says the committee, is that most of the lurid reports confused occasional experimentation with serious involvement. There is no doubt that the occasional or experimental use of cannabis by students has increased significantly. This seems primarily due to peer pressure and curiosity that have been piqued by stimulating publicity. Chronic abuse of the drug, however, is much less frequent than has been reported. While this is encouraging, it cannot be construed to mean that the use of drugs, and of cannabis in particular, has not become an increasing problem over the immediately preceding years. It has, and this increase represents a dangerous trend.

By comparing the various reports it becomes clear that statistics concerning the use of cannabis are as unreliable as statistics collected to establish data on any subject. Happily, the valid reports that have at least some research and direction indicate that students in general are as capable of discerning danger in drug abuse as are their parents. The difference between responses in the two groups is that youth becomes excited over the imposition of restraints while parents panic over maintaining proper controls.

Everybody is not *using* cannabis. The statistics that say they are are misleading. The problem, of course, lies in the definition of the word "using." Occasional experimentation cannot be classified as use. The difference between the occasional user and the chronic abuser is tremendous in that the personal need for a pharmacological crutch with which to escape reality is a major motivating factor in the latter case.

Psychological need has no geographical or ethnic barriers; thus, it is not surprising to find that groups once thought to be impervious to the attractiveness of drug abuse are now becoming major offenders. Cannabis arrests demonstrate this both in number and in type of user. In 1967 arrests rates jumped almost 1,000 percent in some areas over the figures for 1966. 1968 statistics were even higher than 1967. Since certain groups are said to use the drug more than others, it would be helpful if we could identify them and outline characteristics of the user. Unfortunately, if one is at all sophisticated concerning this problem it is impossible to to do this. There was a time, as *Newsweek* has noted, when cannabis was the magic grass of the Negro ghetto, the jazz world, or more recently the hippie community.[9] Today, it has entered the bloodstream of the American middle class. "Marijuana," *Life* magazine says, "long a part of the bohemian scene in the United States, suddenly has become commonplace on college campuses, among intellectuals and suburbanites and, most worrisome of all, even among the subteenagers."[10] In other words, the scene has become ubiquitous and confused.

While we cannot accurately depict the cannabis user as a specific type of individual we can distinguish three major categories in which users fall, based on use activity and motivation for drug abuse. First on the list we find the old group of antisocial misfits, the "lower-caste" group (i.e., uneducated and, usually, unemployed and poorly motivated) who have from the beginning used the drug as an added chorus to an already established refrain of antiauthoritarianism, antidisciplinarianism, and antisocial activities. These are the users the police used to associate with the drug. This picture is so strongly retained by police that many law enforcement personnel still have difficulty recognizing that this group, once the only significant one, has now become the minority.

When this type of user took cannabis he soon found that there were stronger drugs to blot out reality, because cannabis did not provide the effect he wanted. This sort of user wanted a soporific to escape the pressures of life. He still does. That such users are still with us is suggested by recent California statewide police statistics from 1965 through the first half of 1968. In the whole of 1965, cannabis abuse arrests numbered 10,002. During 1966, the arrests totaled 18,243. In 1967, they rose to 37,514. During the *first half* of 1968 (statistics for the last six months are not yet available), cannabis abuse arrests in California totaled a staggering 26,145. Now compare the slow but steady coordinated rise in heroin arrests during the same period in this state: 2,623 in 1965; 2,671 in 1966; 3,494 in 1967; and 2,338 for the *first half* of 1968.[11]

Statistically the California figures mirror the conclusion reached by many law enforcement authorities and others in the field of addiction and drug abuse that a certain group of drug-abuse-prone individuals will begin their pattern with cannabis and progress from this starting point to the abuse of heroin. This hard narcotic is better suited than is cannabis to the demands of these people because it offers, in addition to its soporific effect, a valid criminally sanctioned weapon against society, close association with the true underworld, and, most important, an agent that will blot out rather than enhance reality.

45

Group Two is peopled by an entirely different breed. The difference appears in their choice of drugs and in the reasons that cause them to use drugs. Whereas Group One was formed by "lower-caste trippers," Group Two, although it can enjoy tripping, is far more interested in self-exploration and mind expansion.

The upper-caste hippie belongs to Group Two, although he stands apart from the rest of this segment by his adoption of obvious antisocial protest symbols. In addition to such hippies, we find the intellectuals, pseudointellectuals, and religious and pseudo-religious people. This group tends to pursue a search for inner truth and inner peace. They share the common denominator of being dissatisfied, bored, curious, and in desperate need of finding something different to experience. When members of this group discover the effects of cannabis are becoming prosaic, they tend, along with the lower-caste hippie who, in other ways belongs more to the first category, to progress to the use of stronger hallucinogens such as LSD, DMT, STP, and others.

Group Three is actually the largest of the three. It is composed primarily of average, curious, uninhibited people out for a lark. These youngsters are usually "chippers," that is, they play with the drug now and then as the mood directs them. Seldom if ever do they become addicted to the drug itself, although by proximity if nothing else they inherit some of the complications and disadvantages of using illegal drugs.

In a way, Group Three people might be described by the anecdote of the mother who took her child to the psychoanalyst each week for therapy, which consisted of the analyst's reading comic books aloud to the child. After an hour or so, the psychiatrist would dismiss the child, directing the mother to return for another session. Soon, the mother began to object to this procedure. "Just why do you do this sort of thing?" she demanded. "Madam," the analyst replied, "you fail to comprehend the problem. We've got to keep reading these comics to your son until we find out why he wants me to do it." The mother threw up her hands in disgust. "For heaven's sake," she said, "I can tell you that. He wants you to read to him because he enjoys the stories."

Although many reasons can be advanced for the growing number of people who are playing with cannabis, the simple yet totally unacceptable fact to many adults is that most young people are using it because effects experienced by using the drug and the excitement occasioned by their use of it are agreeable in themselves. They enjoy seeing adults turn pale with rage and impotent in their attempts to control the problem. Then, too, they enjoy playing with the effects of the drug.

Smoking cannabis is a modish way to get the attention of society and to watch one's parents go berserk. In fact, many youngsters possess the drug without any real plans to use it. One fifteen-year-old apprehended by police made this fact plain to his arresting officers: "Honest," he said, "I don't plan on smoking the stuff; I just keep it around as a status symbol." Of course this is not always the case.

Many observations have been offered by various authorities about the users belonging to Group Three. Most of these opinions seem to be based on biased, subjective, unsubstantiated observations. Some adults assume these youths automatically become social misfits the minute they pick up a joint. Others promote the idea that no harm occurs to those who merely play with cannabis. Both arguments are wrong.

While kids are kids and each is a story unto himself, there are several reasonably correct observations that can be made about this group as a whole. First, they are not bad. They come from what is currently accepted as good homes. They may turn out to be Sam or Joe or Sally or Jane from across the street. They may even be our own children. Only a few of these youngsters will progress to the constant use of other dangerous drugs. In saying this, however, we must keep in mind that the potential of such progression is always there because of the ready availability of more dangerous drugs and the presence of peer-group pressure which constantly reassures newcomers. "Nothing can go wrong (except getting busted)," the newcomers are told "because small amounts of these drugs can't hurt you."

Most of these users will emerge from their drug experience without any apparent harm either to themselves or to society. Unless they slip into the drug abuse pattern seen in Group

One and Group Two, few will continue to abuse cannabis once the fad is over and the communications media find something more newsworthy.

Meantime, what is the nature of the world of marijuana to which all types of users are exposed to one degree or another? And what is the nature of the marijuana experience which enthusiasts praise so highly? These questions will form the subject of the rest of this chapter.

The Language of the Marijuana World

"The world of marijuana," Cohen says, "is a state within a state, a culture within a culture, and it is impossible to estimate its population."[12] This world has its own etiquette, its ethics, its pattern of survival, and its jargon. A knowledge of these factors is essential for an understanding of this subculture and the people who inhabit it. First, the jargon.

Cannabis (marijuana, marajuana, marihuana) has, as we have noted, numerous synonyms. The same holds true for the people who use it. The more common descriptive terms for the user today is "head," in this case "pothead," or "weed head." He may also be called a "roach bender," "tea man," "weed hound" or numerous other terms that might be popular in a particular community of users at any given time. The word "head" is more versatile than other names since it can be used to denote any drug-taker; those who use LSD are termed "acid heads," opium users, "hop heads," and so forth.

The marijuana cigarette is probably blessed with as many nicknames as the weed itself. It is referred to as a "reefer," "rocket," "stick," "joint," or "weed." Once it has burned to a tiny butt it is known as a "roach." Because the tetrahydrocannabinols tend to accumulate in this small tip, roaches are prized by users. Such a reefer butt really looks like a cockroach and doubtless acquired its name from this resemblance. The association of the two inspired at least one song prior to the acid-rock days about a groovy cockroach who could not get through the day without using marijuana. You may have sung "La Cucaracha" without realizing its meaning.

With the entrance of the intellectual into the cannabis drug community a caste system has evolved. Basically there are two

48

castes, an upper and a lower. Each is characterized by the way the user enjoys his drug. The lower-caste user is totally unconcerned about the intellectual advantages of philosophizing and self-exploration which intrigue his educated counterpart. The lower-caste user simply "trips," that is, he experiences the bizarre effect of the drug for the effect alone. The word *trip* can generally be defined as a psychological excursion produced by the intake of a drug or drugs, during which interval the individual enjoys, or endures, certain ideas and mental and sensory effects. Until recently, when the high school, college, and postgraduate crowd entered the drug arena, most cannabis users were lower-caste users, both as to their origins and as to their mode of use of the drug.

The upper caste, still growing in size and now the major contemporary group, is composed of intellectuals—students, professionals, artists, musicians, actors, and professors, who take the drug to "maintain" and to explore themselves and the infinite. To "maintain" in this parlance is to defer the enjoyment of the pleasurable effects of the drug and to utilize the experience to better understand one's inner self and rid oneself of his "hangups." This is not to imply that the upper-caste user does not "trip." He does. Not infrequently this is his principal goal at a given cannabis session. But whereas the upper-caste user will both trip and maintain, the lower-caste user seldom sees any benefit in maintaining per se. This user considers cannabis primarily as fun or as a recreational or escapist thing to enjoy without the complications of intellectual overtones.

A "hangup" in the world of cannabis, and in the world of hallucinogens in general, is a psychological problem that prevents one from arriving at the desired state of ultimate composure, or of "being cool." A hangup differs from a "hassle," another unpleasant experience, in that the hassle is usually an interpersonal squabble of varying intensity.

There are four states of being, with gray zones in between, which characterize the relationships of the user of cannabis to society in general and to his fellow users in particular. They are: "cool," "groovy," "hip," and "square."

At the bottom of the social ladder we find the square. The square is seldom if ever cool. He is "not with it," that is, he doesn't know "what's happening" (what's going on around him, particularly as it relates to the drug community). Worse, he probably doesn't realize his sad situation inasmuch as he is immersed in such activities as paying the rent, fixing the car, and raising a family. With rare exceptions, people over thirty-five are square.

A rung up the ladder we find the "hip." The hip individual is one who may or may not be out of the age group where "it's happening," he may or may not take part in the action. But he knows "where it's at" (he is aware of the situation). The true hip is not only savvy but probably approves of the action. If he is a straight hip he knows but either ignores or disapproves of these drug activities. If, on the other hand, he casts a tolerant or friendly eye on the goings-on, he is a groovy hip or sometimes, groovy hippy. In any case, the hip is not to be confused with the Haight-Ashbury type of hippie who is a breed unto himself.

Near the top of the ladder we find the truly groovy individual. He is aware of the "scene" (the overall picture) as is the hippy, but he differs in that he delights in indulging in the action with the rest of the "cats" (users). Whereas the groovy cat is always hip, the hip individual may not be capable of grooving and he may or may not be cool. For, as we shall see, cool people may groove but groovy people may not necessarily reach the state of being cool. Not infrequently the groovy person fails to attain the cool state because of his hangups, the principal one being that he prefers to trip rather than to maintain.

The word *groove,* incidentally, may also be used to describe the ability of two or more people to communicate with seemingly total rapport. Thus, as two people sit and "rap" (express serious, usually personal thoughts, preferably without hypocritical overtones), they find themselves in such accord that they begin to "groove."

The cool individual is at the top of the heap. He "has it made" because he has conquered, at least in his own opinion, all his hangups. He not only knows what's happening but he knows where it's at. He can maintain or trip; he can groove or he can cool it. You ask him for an opinion and he let's you have it with no hassle or pretense. In user's parlance, he "lets it all hang out."

In a more conforming idiom, the cool individual is one who is capable of existing in reality because he understands himself and his problems. More important, he understands the problems of his fellow human beings and accepts both the person and his hangups for what they are, without censure. If he departs from this condition of tolerance and acceptance and expresses himself without maintaining control over his emotions, he is said to have "blown his cool." If this happens, it is usually due to a resurgence of one of his hangups.

Parents will recognize that this terminology is also a part of many teenagers' vocabularies. It varies from place to place and individual to individual. Newer terms such as "clean," "righteous," "boss," and others have come in to give competition to "cool." No one knows from one minute to the next what term will survive and what one will fold. As soon as the older generation begins to employ current terms they lose their adolescent appeal and soon are discarded.

Confusion in the use and study of this terminology becomes increasingly great in direct proportion to the squareness of the individual. At the moment it is contemporary teenage thinking to consider parents "square." Parents are supposed to lack the quality of universal tolerance which precludes their being truly cool or inclines them toward "blowing" whatever little cool they might possess when faced with their children's often erratic behavior. Most adults ignore and deplore this jargon. The lower-caste weed head uses it as part of his subcultural language. The high-caste weed head, however, and particularly the high-caste acid head, both employ and purposefully define these terms as they relate drug users to society.

GETTING AND SPENDING

Before one can turn on to cannabis he has to have a supply. There are basically four ways he can do this. He can grow cannabis himself, smuggle it over the border if he lives close to Mexico, acquire it from a user friend or group of users, or he can buy it.

51

Growing one's own for fun and profit is easy enough since cannabis grows readily in any kind of soil. Thus the gardener with the blackest of thumbs can sow his seed in the spring and harvest it three months later. He cuts off the flowering tops, partially dries them in the sun or the oven, or he may take them to the laundromat, as did one enterprising young man, and toss them into the dryer (with the heat set at "Cotton"). Then he's ready to roll his own. The fact that more people do not grow their own supply is to be credited to the omnipresent police, who are ever on the lookout for the tall, ornamental weed. These men—commonly referred to as "fuzz," "the man," or "heat" by the cannabis crowd—are eagles at detecting marijuana growths of any size. As an example, in the summer of 1967 a young man leased a thirty-five acre farm outside Washington, D.C., in suburban Virginia, and seeded one acre in cannabis. At current market prices his acre would have yielded him a return of something like a hundred thousand dollars. But before that could happen narcotics agents found the planting and arrested the grower. For good measure, the agents informed the grower he had planted his seed too late and frost would have killed the plants before they could be harvested.[13]

If growing cannabis is hazardous, smuggling is worse. It is true that customs and narcotics agents cannot possibly catch all the cannabis that tumbles past the wide-open border gates between the United States and Mexico, but they make a sufficiently successful effort so that most people hesitate to take a risk that could send them to prison for as long as ten years. Moreover, many Mexican suppliers cheerfully turn in the occasional buyers, whom they won't see again anyway, and collect from narcotics agents a sum based on the value of the contraband. Even so, enough people make it through so that others are tempted to follow suit.

Constant borrowing from friends causes the usual kinds of friction. Some people are fortunate enough to be supplied without complaints by friends, lovers, or even parents. In Los Gatos, California, juvenile authorities encountered such a family of users. Truant officers called for help from narcotics agents when they sought an explanation for the continual absence from school of four children. The agents visited the home, a mountain cabin, inhabited by a thirty-eight-year-old father, his twenty-eight-year-old wife and five children, aged four through fourteen. The father was kneeling in the rain on the front lawn, his eyes gazing skyward. "I can see the Resurrection taking place," he informed the officers. Inside, agents found the children, one of whom offered the information: "My Daddy puts LSD in my soda pop so we can turn on as a family." The wife added, "Sometimes the kids keep their own bags of grass." The nine-year-old volunteered that he had taken thirteen trips that week and was accustomed to sharing his supply with fellow students at school. During the booking of the parents on charges of possession of marijuana and contributing to the delinquincy of minors, the police unearthed the information that two weeks previously the husband had shot his wife in the leg when he was "high" and had summarily taken care of the problem by digging the bullet out with his hunting knife. This family that smoked together did not stay together.[14]

If families don't supply it, young people occasionally can acquire it at "pot parties." Some pot shindigs have occurred under the very noses of innocent parents, such as a recent case in suburban Connecticut where parents held a party for their daughter's seventeenth birthday, only to find a total of 170 teenagers overrunning the house and filling it with heavy smoke. While the adults remained ignorant of the nature of the smoke, police did not. They raided the party, booked the mother and some seventy young people in what was the largest raid to date involving teenage drug users in the state of Connecticut.[15]

But it is generally agreed that the most common way of acquiring a "stash" (private supply) of marijuana is to "cop" (buy) it. It takes little effort to find a seller today, unless you happen to be over thirty-five or a newcomer to town. Sellers are suspicious of older buyers or persons obviously unacquainted with the area. But persistence will usually find a careless seller who is himself primarily a user. Careless sellers last only a short while. In time they usually sell to a narcotics agent and their peddling days are over. It takes some familiarity with an area and the presentation of the right attitude before the unknown buyer can make the necessary contacts to acquire his own marijuana.

An instance of the crude buyer was recently brought to the attention of the author on a visit to the San Francisco's Haight-Ashbury district. A hippie who peddled underground newspapers claimed that a now-aging actress had just slipped him a five and asked where the "grass action" was, that is, the action of buying and selling cannabis. The hippie told her, "I don't know nobody that's holding" (anyone with a supply of marijuana). He pointed her out down the street where, with her two male escorts, she was still pressing her search for a "lid" (a supply sufficient to make two or three dozen reefers).

For many people the act of buying cannabis is more exciting than actually smoking it. They find a certain thrill in the game of "narco versus narks" (addict versus narcotics agents). Normally they are looking only for small amounts of cannabis, or for "bag or box action," "lid or tin action," or occasionally "pound action." Such terms refer to the amount of marijuana being bought and sold at a given time. These volume measurements, confusing to the uninitiated but clear to the user, are usually constant throughout the United States. What varies is the price and the quality which are determined by supply and demand, season, and source. Supply is dependent upon the season of the year (cannabis is most plentiful in the fall), locale (the nearer to the Mexican border, the cheaper it usually is), and the intensity of local police activity. As for for quality, some connections are more reputable than others.

In general, a bag or box is a small amount, usually enough to stuff into a penny matchbox. The price is from five to ten dollars, hence the terms nickel or dime bags. Sufficient cannabis is contained in this amount to make about eight skimpy cigarettes, or joints. The next size up is the lid or can. This is approximately an ounce and comes wrapped in a plastic bag or in an old tobacco can. Cans are of two sizes, short (loosely packed) and long (tightly packed). They vary in price from ten to thirty dollars, depending on local conditions. If one has "a half a C" ($50.00) he can buy a pound which is sufficient weed so that if he wants to repack it he can make a thousand dollars profit from his original investment.

There seems to be no set rule for wrapping marijuana for sale. Large quantities may come wrapped in newspaper or packed into attaché cases. In a recent diplomatic flurry, a foreign agent was caught bringing in a whole case full of cannabis under his arm. Small quantities may be placed between the pages of a book, put into cigarette packages, or wherever human ingenuity contrives to conceal them.

A recent advertisement in a Los Angeles underground newspaper could revolutionize the whole picture. It offered two hundred factory-rolled, king-sized cigarette papers with the brand name and crest stamped in gold on each. "Mom will never know unless she smokes it," the ad read. "Turn your mother on! She'll think it's a carton of regular cigarettes. Simply fill with your brand. Gruvy for business meetings, church or your next coffee break. Society will think you have gone legit."[16]

As for sellers, they can be anybody from a teenager to a grandmother. Few people, however, sell cannabis as a profession. Most do it for the excitement, for a rapid intake of cash, or for a lark. Often they determine to sell until approached by a stranger, which is a deadly sign that the seller has been spotted or become known.

Much petty peddling is done by teenage users. In Van Nuys, California, police apprehended a fifteen-year-old girl selling $2.00 worth to a girlfriend. The transaction took place in the girls' restroom during nutrition class.[17] In Salt Lake City, police apprehended a sixteen-year-old boy who was selling asthmatic tobacco and claiming it was cannabis. Some two hundred people had purchased from this boy, and they were so eager to have the drug that they did not know it was merely a substitute. They got their high, although for some it was more than they bargained for. The substitute he gave them contained substances that were extremely toxic if used in large quantities. They were capable of producing a "high" complete with hallucinations and, for some, toxic psychoses. In fact, several deaths have now been reported throughout the nation as a result of the abuse of asthmatic tobacco.[18]

Not all who sell are users. One apparently troubled youth wrote a nationally syndicated religious columnist stating he had a friend who got his supply from a brother in the merchant marine and who was making a tidy sum reselling it. He wrote the columnist inquiring if it would be proper to do this himself to earn money to go to college. "I'm trying to tell myself there is nothing wrong with this," he philosophized. "After all, I don't make those kids smoke the stuff. They do it of their own free will. Besides I have read it doesn't harm you."[19] Many others have read the same thing. With consistent reassurance from various communication media that the drug is harmless and laws controlling it stupid, they have decided that the psychedelic minority cannot be wrong, and so they try to pick up some extra money from those who are looking for a supply.

Though numerous cases of teenage sellers could be cited, none is more poignant than that recorded by *Los Angeles Times* reporter George Reasons[20] concerning Johnny, age sixteen, who had a going business established among his friends. "I tried pot a couple of times but I didn't like it," the youth told police. "There were others who did, though. They wanted pot. I had pot. I didn't twist anybody's arm. I didn't turn anybody on. I didn't drum up the action. They came to me. It was strictly business. I didn't try to sell to them. I don't think kids ought to use it."

Johnny was one of nineteen arrested in his school for peddling drugs, after police invested some four hundred man-hours of time to establish their case. The boy sold his joints to fellow students for a dollar each, a bit higher than the usual going rate. From this trade he managed to stash away about $700 before his arrest. John, who came from a respectable middle-class family, as did the other pushers, had a particular reason for wanting the cash: "I got interested in auto racing a few months ago," he explained, "I had started saving my profits to buy a car."

John was so discreet in setting up his sales that school authorities had no idea their halls were frequently the scenes of drug contacts. Because of his caution he sold no drugs at school, preferring to make deliveries off campus. That police ever discovered the situation was due primarily to a break that occurred during an investigation of a minor traffic violation. The arrested juvenile, once he began talking, was a veritable fountain of information. He told police all he knew about narcotics operations in his school and offered to introduce a young deputy undercover man to the proper people.

Once the deputy managed to work his way in, he discovered these young peddlers worked primarily out of a drive-in hamburger stand and a local bowling alley. Not content with selling cannabis, they peddled everything from pep pills to hard narcotics. Teenagers came from all over the county to buy from them. Each of these pushers—seven under age eighteen, eleven barely past that age—worked together, sold to the same customers, yet maintained their separate business operations. Parents were astounded after the arrests. A police officer told Reasons: "With present laws, we can't stamp out the problem. All we can expect to do is control it to the best of our ability."

Though petty pushers of cannabis tend to limit their sales activities to a few friends or known customers, some sellers mimic the big time. These people deal in kilos (a little over two pounds) bought with a ritual reminiscent of the days of Al Capone. The large purchases are then divided for greater profits to be made from individual sales. Such deals are usually made by a contact introducing a potential buyer and seller. Only first names are used, and no questions asked as to source of supply or the way it was brought in. The purchase is made either by putting the money in front (presale payment) or on credit, if the customer is well known. Delivery is then set for some future date. On the day of pickup, the buyer is notified of the drop, told to be there at a given time, and the deal is completed.

Most of the larger sales are made at night, either in a home or in the back of an automobile. If the sale is made in a home, the homeowner or apartment lessee usually gets a cut of the purchase for his hospitality. If the deal is made in a car it is usually an old car, since the police are authorized to seize and hold any automobile used in illegal transactions involving narcotic drugs.

Some writers suggest that a large organized criminal group is in charge of marijuana sales. This has not been proven. Several factors work against this. Cannabis, truly a weed, is too easy to grow and the supply from Mexico is plentiful. There are, in addition, other sources available to those in the know which make the marijuana business essentially a small-operator affair. Moreover, the money is greater in other types of drug exchange. The result is that marijuana traffic cannot be controlled simply by attacking major crime syndicates.

ROLLING YOUR OWN

Once the buyer acquires his supply he takes it home and hides it. Such individual deposits are referred to as "stashes." When it is needed for smoking a portion is removed from the stash, manicured, and rolled into joints, unless the smoker prefers to put it in a pipe. Manicuring can be quite a process. One of the nation's news magazines (rapidly becoming known as an accurate source for the "how to" of drug abuse) suggests that the user force the cutting through a number-twelve mesh protective screen, such as that used in prison and detention homes, take out the stems and seeds, roll, ignite, and puff off to cloud nine.

Once rolled, however, it is not simply a question of puffing away. To smoke marijuana and acquire its effects requires a special technique. Cannabis cannot be mixed with cigarette tobacco for the purpose of turning on innocent youth. This is an old fable spawned by misinformation. The person who smokes cannabis knows very well what he is doing because the procedure requires his full attention and time until he becomes intoxicated. Although an increasing number of smokers are "going up" alone, cannabis smoking tends to be a social affair; users prefer to be with others during the trip.

Usually several smokers will meet in a room (teapad) or in a car. Sometimes they hole up in a closet for a better effect, since the fumes tend to concentrate in a small area. The holder of the marijuana then begins the ritual. He takes the reefer, which he has probably rolled himself, and inspects it for flaws. It is, in most cases, a skinny cigarette double wrapped usually in wheat paper and kept small on purpose since it burns more rapidly, is less expensive than thick joints, and can be consumed to its bitter end.

It is important that the twigs have not perforated the paper, since this makes smoking more difficult and wastes the active ingredient. The ends have to be checked to make sure they are tucked in tightly so that the ingredients won't fall out while the cigarette is being passed around. These joints are far from being like their tailor-made commercial cigarette counterparts. Since they are irregular and uneven, it is common for one end of the reefer to draw more easily than the other. The smokers determine this before settling down to smoke.

Rosevear describes the use of the marijuana cigarette with compelling accuracy. After selecting the end to be lighted, he advises, the smoker wets the skinny weed down with spit. He may roll it around in a trough of spit puddled in his protruded lower lip; He may lick it sloppy with his tongue; or he may "let it all slide in." Rosevear continues: "Often the joint is a grey, soggy thing, repulsive looking, sad and unsanitary but the wetting moistens the joint and slows down the burning process."[21]

It is now time to light up. Even here the process is complicated. If the lighted end is not started correctly it won't burn evenly. This means that some of the cigarette could be wasted and the smoking time shortened. Additionally, smoke from poorly lighted cigarettes will often burn hot and be unpleasant to the taste. It is important, from an economic as well as a pleasure standpoint, that the smoker learn to light his fire properly. The best way is to hold the cigarette at eye level, center the flame and turn the cigarette slowly, twisting it back and forth to assure even distribution of the flame.

Once the joint is lit it is kept in constant use. Each smoker drags deeply on it, holding the smoke in his lungs and flushing it down with short breaths, until he has filled his lungs to capacity. They then sit and wait for the "stuff to have a chance," which means to hold it as long and as deeply in the lungs as is possible in order to effect rapid and full alveolar transfer of the tetrahyrocannabinols to the bloodstream. "The object of marijuana smoking," advises Rosevear, "is to get the smoke into the lungs in the most efficient way, taste and flavor be damned. The throat is opened and the smoke drawn directly into it."

In a few short minutes the joint burns down to a butt. This

butt is referred to as a "roach" and is a very valuable item in the world of marijuana since it is loaded with tetrahydro-cannabinols that have concentrated there during the smoking. The roach, however, is very tiny and very hot to handle. To enjoy it one must hold it with a paper clip, tweezers, stick a pin through it, or, if one is very sophisticated, retain it with a jewel-bedecked roachholder. The latter is available in most psychedelic shops that sell all accessories for marijuana smoking but the weed itself.

Even with the holder the roach is too hot to hold to the lips. To overcome this it is held close to the mouth and the smoke is drawn in by a current of air caused by rapid inhalation through pursed lips. These concentrated fumes, like the others, are held deeply in the lungs as long as possible to acquire the full effect.

There are also many other ways of smoking pot. It can be smoked with special holders made from cardboard and foil, which permit an air-smoke mixture, or smoked in special or regular pipes with or without tobacco. The roach may be smoked as mentioned above or put into the end of a cigarette and taken as a "cocktail." If one prefers he may save roaches and make a full joint out of them when he accumulates enough. The method is the choice of the smoker.

And every smoker is seeking certain sensations. These vary, of course, but they also have certain features in common. To these we turn to see what the marijuana experience is like from the inside.

1. Louis S. Goodman and Alfred Gilman, *The Pharmacological Basis of Therapeutics* (2d ed.; New York: Macmillan, 1955), p. 174.

2. Jerry Cohen, "Marijuana; Views Collide," *Los Angeles Times,* Dec. 4, 1967.

3. David Smith, "Testimony before Assemblyman Pete Wilson," Los Angeles, California, March 1, 1968.

4. Nathan B. Eddy, quoted in "Marijuana Controls," *Los Angeles Times,* Jan. 19, 1968.

5. Joel Fort, quoted in "When patients ask your views on marijuana," *Patient Care,* 1:12 (Dec., 1967).

6. "Survey Shows Use of Drugs by Students," *Los Angeles Times,* Feb. 17, 1967.

7. "4 out of 10 at UC Reported Smoking Marijuana," *Los Angeles Times,* March 30, 1967.

8. *The Dangerous Drug Problem,* Supplementary Report, The Medical Society of the County of New York, June 15, 1966.

9. "The Marijuana Problem," *Newsweek,* July 24, 1967.

10. "Marijuana: Millions of Turned on Users," *Life,* July 7, 1967.

11. Statistics furnished by the Office of the Attorney General, State of California, January, 1968.

12. Sidney V. Cohen, *Uncanny Power of the Hallucinogens: The Drug Takers,* (New York: Time-Life Books, 1965), p. 102.

13. "Hippies' Dream Farm," *Time,* Sept. 8, 1967, p. 17.

14. "Parents Admit to Giving 5 Children LSD, Marijuana," *Los Angles Times,* Jan. 30, 1967.

15. "Teen Party Raided and Dope Seized," *Los Angeles Times,* Nov. 13, 1967.

16. "A Joint/or isnt it?" ad in the *Los Angeles Free Press,* Jan. 26, 1968, p. 25.

17. "Girl 15, Arrested for Marijuana Sale," *Los Angeles Times,* Sept. 23, 1967.

18. "Fake Marijuana Sales Jail Youth," *Los Angeles Times,* Sept. 29, 1967.

19. Norman Vincent Peale, in *Look,* Nov. 7, 1958.

20. George Reasons, "Johnny, 16, Tells His Success Story as a Marijuana Salesman," *Los Angeles Times,* Feb. 24, 1963.

21. John Rosevear, *Pot: A Handbook of Marijuana* (New York: University Books, M67), pp. 66-67.

"What do you suppose Alice used to get to
Wonderland?"

THE MARIJUANA TRIP 4

> *Though nothing can bring back the hour*
> *Of splendor in the grass, of glory in the flower;*
> *We will grieve not, rather find Strength in what remains behind.*
> —William Wordsworth

It should be obvious that cannabis users must experience a highly pleasurable effect since they go to so much trouble and risk to get it. This effect has been described in literature by various writers for the past two thousand years or more with an ecstasy that makes experienced users glow with warm delight and nonusers wonder if they might not have missed something worthwhile. One of the more graphic descriptions was written during the late nineteenth century by the poet Charles Baudelaire, who, with Théophile Gautier, was a founding member of the Club des Hachichins at the Hotel Pimodan in Paris. Baudelaire, it should be remembered, is discussing hashish, which is five to six times stronger than *Cannabis mexicana*. Despite this, his recital is relevant to all cannabis products, for marijuana effects are similar to hashish effects, differing only in intensity of toxicity. This can be demonstrated by increasing the intake of marijuana, for all the cerebrotoxic effects of the hallucinogens, including those of LSD, can be produced by an adequate intake of marijuana.

"What does one experience? What does one see? Wonderful things, amazing sights? Is it very beautiful or very terrible or very dangerous?" These are the questions, says Baudelaire, the nonuser asks about the cannabis experience. They are childish questions, he muses, "such as might be felt by somebody who has never left his fireside on meeting a man returning from distant and unknown lands."[1]

Baudelaire also dispels the illusion that the cannabis trip and sleep are similar. Man's sleep, he says, produces two kinds of dreams. There are those that relate to his ordinary life and those that are "hieroglyphic" dreams. These latter are absurd, unpredictable dreams with no relation to the characters and passions of the dream. The cannabis trip, however, he assures us, is utterly different from these dreams. It does not bring the user beyond the bounds of natural dreams, although the intoxication is in the nature of a vast dream. "It will always," he says, "retain the private tonality of the individual. The man wanted the dream, now the dream will govern the man." He notes, "(Man) wished to ape the angel, he has become an animal; and for a brief while the latter is very powerful—if power is the correct word for an excessive sensibility—because it is subject to no restraining or directing government."[2] Baudelaire makes it quite clear that everyone who wants to use the drug should realize that no miracles will be produced by it. There will only be an exaggeration of the natural. The drug affects the brain and it is the brain of the user which will determine the effects to be experienced:

> A man will never escape from his destined physical and moral temperament; hashish will be a mirror of his impressions and private thoughts, a magnifying mirror, it is true, but only a mirror. . . .
>
> Here, then, is happiness. It is large enough to fill a small spoon. Happiness, with all its intoxications, follies and puerilities. You can swallow it without fear—one does not die of it. Your physical organs will be in no way affected. Later on, perhaps, a too frequent consultation of the oracle will diminish your strength of will; perhaps you will be less of a man than you are today. But the retribution is so distant and the disaster in store for you so difficult to define! What are you risking?[3]

With an awareness that makes him as contemporary in thought as Timothy Leary, Baudelaire warns that "every perfect debauch calls for perfect leisure." It is important when one uses cannabis that he protect himself from noxious influences because the drug not only exaggerates the user's personality, it also distorts the circumstances and surroundings present during the smoking session. It is as true today as it was in Baudelaire's time that one must not burden himself with appointments, he must have no domestic worries, he must be free of unhappy love affairs, if he hopes to have a good trip. "This is most important," Baudelaire warns, "for any grief or spiritual unrest, any memory of an obligation claiming your attention at a fixed time, would toll like a bell amidst your intoxication and poison your pleasure. The unrest would become an agony, the worry a torture."[4] If Baudelaire were alive today and speaking the language of the user, he might put it this way: "any bringdown, any hangups, any hassles can cause a bummer when you're up on weed."

Baudelaire divides the cannabis trip into three different successive phases. They are: going up, experiencing physical and sensory effects, and, finally, hallucination. Beginners, he says, usually complain that nothing is really happening or that, if it is, it is too slow in taking effect. They wait with childish impatience and then, when the drug fails to function fast enough or in the way they think it should, they pretend, acting out what they think the drug should do even though it is not actually doing it. This sort of performance, he says, "gives great delight to old initiates who know just how hashish sets about its work."

When the drug begins to act, Baudelaire warns, it appears like the symptoms of a storm that hovers before it strikes. These symptoms develop and multiply as the incredible situation unfolds. The first symptom is a sort of irrelevant and irresistible hilarity. "Attacks of causeless mirth, of which you are almost ashamed, repeat themselves at frequent intervals, cutting across periods of stupor during which you try in vain to pull yourself together. The simplest words, the most trivial ideas, assume a new and strange guise; you are actually astonished at having hitherto found them so simple. Incongruous and unforeseeable resemblances and comparisons, interminable bouts of punning on words, rough sketches for farces, continually spout from your brain. . . . From time to time you laugh at yourself, at your own silliness and folly; and your companions, if you have such, laugh alike at your condition and at their own. But, since they laugh at you without malice, you laugh back at them without rancor."[5]

The mirth that occurs with cannabis intoxication, Baudelaire continues, "with its alternating spells of languor and convulsion, this distress in the midst of delight, generally lasts only for a fairly short time." Then the coherence of one's ideas becomes so vague, the conducting filament between fancies so thin, that the only ones who can understand the user are other users in the room with him. "And once again, on this question, too," Baudelaire muses, "there is no means of ascertaining the truth; perhaps they only think they understand you and the deception is mutual. This crazy whimsicality, these explosive bursts of laughter, seem like real madness, or at least like a madman's folly, to anyone who is not in the same state as yourself. Conversely, the self-control, good sense and orderly thoughts of a prudent observer who has abstained from intoxication—these delight and amuse you like a special sort of dementia. Your roles are inverted: his calmness drives you to ironic disdain." At this point the ridiculous occurs: "The madman begins to feel sorry for the sane man; and from this moment on the notion of his (the smoker's) own superiority begins to gleam on the horizon of his intellect. Soon it will grow, swell and burst upon him like a meteor."[6]

Once this childish phase is over there is a momentary lull in activity, then various physical sensations begin to occur. With Baudelaire, it was heralded by a sensation of chilliness in the extremities and a great weakness "in all the members." This experience, of course, is variable; each person feels or fails to feel specific sensations depending on his particular trip. Baudelaire went through numerous physical tugs and pulls which are not usually described by cannabis users in this country, but after this period of individual experience his observations are consistent with those given by most contemporary users:

> . . . at this phase of the intoxication a new subtlety or acuity manifests itself in all the senses. This development is common to the senses of smell, sight, hearing and touch. The eyes behold the Infinite. The ear registers almost imperceptive sounds, even in the midst of the greatest din. This is when hallucinations set in. External objects acquire, gradually and one after another, strange new appearances; they become distorted or transformed. Next occur mistakes in the identities of objects, and transposals of ideas. Sounds clothe themselves in color, and colors contain music.[7]

Although this description is over a hundred years old it is still quite accurate for most trips. It should therefore be clear even to the uninitiated that cannabis offers both the curious and the bored a gallery of sensory titillations that make the drug excursion both pleasant and fascinating. But this is not all, for in the last phase of prepsychotic intoxication one sees hallucinations that can be either most pleasant or very horrifying. "It sometimes happens," Baudelaire recounts, "that your personality disappears, and you develop objectivity—that preserve of the pantheistic poets—to such abnormal degree that the contemplation of outward objects makes you forget your own existence, and you soon melt into them. Your eye rests upon an harmoniously shaped tree bowing beneath the wind."

The next thing Baudelaire describes, although it might seem normal to a poet, is not the sort of thing many people experience even in a lifetime of drug use. Personification occurs, and as it does it seems quite real to the cannabis user. "You begin by endowing the tree with your own passions," writes Baudelaire, "your desire or melancholy; its groanings and swayings become your own and soon you *are* the tree." He offers yet another example: "let us suppose that you are sitting and smoking. Your gaze rests a moment too long on the bluish clouds emerging from your pipe. The notion of a slow, steady, eternal evaporation will take hold of your mind, and soon you will apply this notion to your own thoughts and your own thinking substance. By a singular transposition of ideas, or mental play upon words, you will feel that you yourself are evaporating, and that your pipe (in which you are huddled and pressed down like the tobacco) has the strange *power to smoke you.*" Under such conditions, Baudelaire concludes, "you seem to live several men's lives in the space of an hour. You resemble, do you not, a fantastic novel that is being lived instead of being written. . . ."[8]

It is interesting to note how closely contemporary writers agree in essence with the sensations experienced by Baudelaire. On January 19, 1965, a very literate psychoanalyst, Dr. Sheldon Cholst, smoked a hashish cigarette and while under its influence jotted down his impressions. As is the case with many who try the drug a few times, enjoy the trip, and emerge from the experience with the same reasonably stable personality with which they began, Dr. Cholst came out of his experience with an impression that cannabis should be a legal form of recreation. "He who is evil is evil and will do so no matter what job or drug he takes," he says. "If only we could ban evil or the evil ones, we'd have no evil problems."[9]

ANALYZING THE MARIJUANA TRIP

Let us look first at some of the conclusions about the marijuana experience recorded by Dr. Cholst, a proponent of legalized cannabis. "I am writing now of the effect of hashish," he says. "I smoked it in a cigarette. Had some childish thoughts or memories—of me as a child knocking over a refrigerator and then hitting my mother for being mad at me and jumping into the fireplace and emerging unscathed and saying look what a delusion of grandeur I am. Unscathed—I can now do anything." Of this experience he observes:

> So, it makes you a child again—in mind or emotions or soul or unboring restless behaviour. You move easily in thoughts and fantasies—one to another like a child. . . . Thus I was adult and child at the same moment. The fountain of youth has been found. The child lives in a world of wonders, he searches, finds, turns away and is afraid sometimes of being hurt or "put down" by adults. But now he is both—so he feels "high," tall like an adult and yet still a child.[10]

It would appear from these comments that one reaction the cannabis user experiences is a reversal of his thought processes and adult senses of responsibility to a childlike level. Is it not possible that precisely this regression is the factor that makes it so difficult for some to recognize the problem of cannabis abuse once they return from the delightful, synthetic escape to childhood? The user, according to Cholst,

> has turned off adult reality—"what to do, where to go, what am I allowed to do" and has returned to the life of the free, primitive child who wanders in his happiness. . . . One's mind is free to wander, think, and all the restlessness is taken care of in the mind. . . . The limitations of mobility of the adult world (reality, laws, etc.) are gotten rid of. . . . Thus a man who is "stoned" is in a sense desirably paralyzed

(partially or wholly) without the need for that motor activity which is indicative of the adult world.[11]

Once a person is under the influence of cannabis, Cholst observes, he no longer has a need to be concerned about the environmental dangers that previously disturbed him. ". . . in the real world," he says, "the concern with danger, insecurity, fear of evil, have made him dress a certain way, listen to rules, frustrate himself, keep himself from being free—unable to do what he wants when he wants to do it."[12] Cannabis, Cholst says, is a "poisoner of frustrating reality," an "antidote for restlessness that is frustrated," an "instant joy and relaxation," a "chemical age-regression that allows us to be young and old at the same moment of time."[13]

The drug hashish, the "fountain of youth," "causes no harm," he concludes, "for what harm is there in being a child in the heart and in the mind . . .?" Cholst seems to have little patience with those who are not willing to try the hashish trip. "Those who do not have this capacity," he says, "those who are too square, too limited, too conformist, too brainwashed, not too bright, these people want the closed-in adult life. . . . These people who either constitutionally or environmentally cannot or do not want this release into childhood life—they will not 'turn on,' they will not feel 'high.' By and large," he argues, "those who wish to smoke already do, but there are some on the borderline who are too afraid they will like it too much and be drawn into the artistic or free life thus losing out on their Faustian bargain. They have sold their souls (their honesty, their desire for freedom, their insistence on truth, honor, dignity for all mankind) for the mess of pottage called financial success, prestige, and acceptance by society."[14]

Since Cholst's observations were made prior to the hippie movement, one cannot identify him with that group. But it is striking to find that the same philosophy is widely voiced by hippies who have taken the cannabis path. There is indeed a kind of conformity about it.

Cholst's praise for cannabis is so persuasive and his denunciation of the nonuser so pungent that nonusers may easily be cowed into silence. But the question that even Cholst's observations will not down is: how far can one go with cannabis before an irreversible disorientation and dissociation takes over? For even reality, not to mention fantasy, can dull the spirit, as in the syndrome of the so-called "Polynesian paralysis." This form of indolence affects many Caucasians who stay too long in the South Pacific. Writing of this phenomenon on the island of Bora Bora, Coles Phinizy says:

> Because they are both beautiful and bountiful, many of the small Polynesian islands that litter the South Pacific are dangerous places. At first sight of such beguiling shores, too many men fall in love and jump ship, foolishly believing that they have found a paradise where the mangoes are never wormy and worrying is against the law.
>
> On any of a hundred Polynesian islands noted for their largess, a man—if he is not careful—can waste away in the midst of plenty. Although an island rat can get along on the fruit of a single palm, a man who tries to do so usually finds he cannot live by coconuts alone. . . . The man who goes to paradise to spend the rest of his days quite often finds after only a month that his senses are surfeited and starting to decay. The hibiscus and the dancing colors of the lagoon fade and are wasted on the eye. In time even the mango loses its taste and only the worm remains. Although none of the island songs mentions it, it is a fact that paradise has a sneaky way of turning a complex man into a discontented vegetable.[15]

If overexposure to an excess of natural beauty can do this, when the mind is presumably operating normally, it can certainly be argued that overstimulation of one's sensory faculties by psychotoxic drugs can do at least the same, if not worse. The effect with drugs, however, is likely to be quicker and more lasting.

How far can one go in his search for total freedom from responsibility and for a childlike response? This depends to a great extent upon the individual and the society that must tolerate and care for him if he decides to drop out. While men like Dr. Cholst may take the cannabis trip and apparently emerge with a continued dedication to the realities of life, there may be far more who cannot make this transition; such persons may become social nonentities or liabilities, and cannabis will have been the agent that turned a productive person into a useless social burden.

When one decides to take a trip with cannabis he can expect to feel the first sensations within minutes after smoking his cigarette. There is no specific pattern of behavior to be anticipated, however, since cannabis has both excitatory and depressant activity. Its effects will vary from time to time and place to place and from person to person. The singularly distinguishing feature of cannabis use is its unpredictability of effect for each person. This must be emphasized, despite the assurance of some writers who imply that each trip on cannabis is identically the same and thus predictable in effect. If each trip were always the same, the use of cannabis would soon become prosaic. Even in the face of the variety of cannabis effects, many persons find it necessary, once the cannabis experience becomes too definable, to go on to something else more stimulating in order to gratify their psychological needs. In this regard, even Rosevear, of all people, admits: "One must realize that any recorded effects are subject to the poetic license and accuracy of the narrator (and to his memory) as well as to the intensity of intoxication."[16]

It is odd but true that some people are so constituted that they cannot derive significant effects from mild cannabis intoxication. Baudelaire noticed this long ago among hashish users. If it is true with hashish it is even truer with the use of less potent cannabis. When the effects fail to occur the frustrated user has the choice of trying to fool himself and his friends, quit, or try something stronger.

In any event, the more common reaction to smoking cannabis is the rapid onset of a feeling of "inner joy" that is totally out of proportion to apparent motivation. The user soon finds himself dreaming, relaxing, lolling in the delicious state of effortless nothingness produced by the drug. It is inaccurate, however, to assume that this is always the case, for some people become quite agitated during the early stages of the cannabis trip. This reaction, however, is not seen in the majority of users.

The delightful state produced by cannabis is referred to as being "high." If the intoxication becomes intense the feeling is described as being "stoned." If the user is alone he may "trip off" and be quiet and drowsy. In company he may be talkative and hilarious. Ideas begin to flit through his mind almost uncontrollably, flashing like bolts of lightning, often illuminating but seldom striking home. The flow of thoughts for some is so overwhelming that, try as they may, they cannot communicate their ideas. This usually strikes the user as hilariously funny, and he begins to titter the high-pitched, giggly laughter so common to cannabis users.

Some beginners need an unusually large amount of cannabis to attain the state of being high. Acknowledging this, Rosevear[17] (who also admits that the only typical and predictable action of a marijuana smoker is the smoking of marijuana) assures his readers that, if the correct smoking procedure is followed, the desired mental effects will present themselves. "Ideas about a variety of subjects continue to flow in a disrupted sequence," he says. "They are usually connected with the smoker's activities prior to smoking. Some events obscurely hidden in the past will be clearly brought to mind, yet transactions and activities only a few seconds old are likely to be forgotten. . . . It is not uncommon for a smoker to stop talking in the middle of a sentence and ask his companions what he was talking about, and very often no one in the group can remember."[18]

As the intoxication progresses and the senses become acutely aware, touch and perception become considerably altered and time and space seem distorted and unimportant. "Man," an adolescent user once said, "when I'm up on weed I'm really living. I float up and up and up until I'm miles above the earth. Then, Baby, I begin to come apart. My fingers leave my hands, my hands leave my wrists, my arms and legs leave my body, and I just floooooat all over the universe."[19] A user may become quite uncoordinated as time goes on, although he himself may fail to recognize it. His complex intellectual capacities are impaired, particularly his speed and accuracy. Walking up the stairs or climbing into a car, for instance, can become interminable journeys complicated by stumbling, slow, uneasy movements. Obviously then, situations that require little or no physical effort are best suited to the cannabis trip; television, listening to music, or just sitting around are the preferred activities. Playing games that require decision or skill is usually a poor occupation for cannabis users since both movement and decision are hampered. A chess game, for example, can go on for hours because the user may contemplate a particular move for an interminable time. If his opponent is also on a trip he rarely minds.

The basic personality of the individual is apparently not appreciably altered by using cannabis. His behavioral reactions may change, however, because of reduced inhibitions and a changed interpretation of events. This is often touted as an advantage but it may be a very real disadvantage if one's basic personality is antisocial and hostile to begin with, as is the case of many who are drawn to the continued use of this drug.

The use of cannabis promotes a feeling of self-confidence that is usually, if not always, unwarranted. The user acquires a feeling of exultation and omnipotence, but such a sensation can quickly dissipate as a result of some negative factor and be replaced by feelings of anxiety and paranoia. Such feelings and the trip they occur on are referred to as a "bring down" and a "bummer."

As the user continues going up (or down) his judgment and memory become impaired. He soon is easily irritated and may, if sufficiently intoxicated, become confused, disoriented, afraid, and filled with an apprehension he may die. Behavior is impulsive and mood reactions are variable. Not infrequently the user experiences phantasmagoria (i.e., the sensation that figures are dwindling into the distance or rushing toward him at tremendous speed, increasing in size as they approach). As one user put it, "It's like looking through the zoom lens on a camera."

With increasing doses hallucinations may appear. If they are pleasant the user will usually trip on them and remain high. If they are unpleasant he may experience deathly fear. If the proper personality indulges in an adequate amount of drug at the proper time, he may enter a true psychotic state. Hallucinations that occur during this state are most unpredictable and sometimes have a depressing tone. An eastern university professor, for example, tried to approach the drug scientifically by inhaling a large amount of a potent form of it. In his mind he developed a pair of blue wings, leapt into an inkwell and flew around, and was trapped inside it for some two hundred years before his power to reason returned sufficiently to permit him to escape.[20]

A cannabis trip usually lasts from three to six hours following cessation of intake of the drug. By twelve hours all symptoms but a slight lethargy and hunger are gone. These are the most usual durations, but some cannabis illusions may linger for some time. "I was in the country one weekend," a jazz musician commented after a cannabis trip. "I was standing by the dresser when I noticed my body lying over there on the bed. I buried my body in the woods. Then I got on the train and came back to town. Since then I have been a soul."[21]

Such a bizarre response to cannabis by persons who are not otherwise abnormal is a recognized phenomenon by students of pharmacology. One of the most common is the user's insistence that he has communed with God, gotten in tune with the universe, or in some similar manner explored the mystic and occult. No matter how much evidence is accumulated to disprove these reactions, the person who experienced them is so thoroughly convinced that it is virtually impossible to shake him from his belief. On some occasions, however, men have been sufficiently objective in their research so that they have been able to prove to themselves and others that most, if not all, of the drug-produced psychic "miracles" are in essence adverse drug or psychotoxic reactions. Of the numerous examples of this sort the following were brought to the author's attention by psychiatrist Charles Wahl and they may stand for the results of objective research into the cannabis experience.[22]

The first is told about veteran physician Oliver Wendell Holmes and involves his experiences under nitrous oxide anesthesia. It was administered for a tooth extraction and the experience that Holmes had under the drug was so powerful that when he emerged he believed he had been given a miraculous revelation of tremendously important social dimensions. Since he could not recapture the vision he persuaded his dentist to reinduce him with the gas so he could know it again. As he was going under he called for a pencil. His face was transfixed by the power of his vision. Before he lost consciousness he wrote his message, and when he came to he called for the paper to see what he had written. The paper read: "Lord, what a stench!"

In another instance a woman had similar convictions while having a dream. She also grabbed paper and pencil and wrote down her discovery before lapsing back into sleep. In the morning she seized the paper to read her revelation. It was: "Hogamus, higamus, men are polygamous. Higamus, hogamus, women monogamous."

Wahl was able to make the same sort of experiment as Doctor Holmes and the woman, but in this case on three cannabis users who were convinced, as are other users, that the insights achieved under the influence of the drug transcend anything accessible by other means. The psychiatrist tape-recorded their conversation when they were on a trip. Later, when they played back the tape, one youth was so disappointed and appalled by the verbal drivel coming from the recorder that he sat down and wept.

"The psychiatrist," Wahl notes, "is forced to the answers that Euclid gave to Ptolemy I, who was interested in learning geometry but who wanted to do it the easy way. Euclid said to him, 'There is no royal road to geometry.' " Drugs, this psychiatrist says, cannot create human ego-strength or personality. They may temporarily warm the user, but when he emerges from his drug-induced dream he is colder and more empty than he ever was before he went up on his poison.

Some time ago a sententious poet wrote a brief verse for the *New Yorker* in which he echoed Margaret Fuller's celebrated nineteenth-century comment, "I accept the Universe." The line has some relevance for those who feel they must escape the world through the use of drugs. Then, in a marked library copy, a whimsical reader, who knew his Victorian history, added a remark to the poet's observation which was the reply Thomas Carlyle made to Margaret Fuller: "You had damned well better!"

1. Charles Baudelaire, *The Essence of Laughter and Other Essays* and *Journals and Letters,* quoted in *The Drug Experience,* edited by David Ebin (New York: The Orion Press, 1961), p. 19.

2. *Ibid*, p. 20.

3. *Ibid.*, p. 20.

4. *Ibid.*, p. 21.

5. *Ibid.*, p. 21.

6. *Ibid.*, p. 22.

7. *Ibid.*, p. 27.

8. *Ibid.*, p. 28.

9. Sheldon Cholst, "Notes on the Use of Hashish," in *The Marihuana Papers,* edited by David Solomon (Indianapolis: Bobbs-Merrill, 1966), p. 221.

10. *Ibid.*, p. 217.

11. *Ibid.*, p. 217.

12. *Ibid.*, p. 218.

13. *Ibid.*, p. 219.

14. *Ibid.*, p. 219.

15. Coles Phinizy, "Bora-Bora: A Paradise on a Precipice," *Sports Illustrated,* Jan. 15, 1968, p. 25.

16. John Rosevear, *Pot: A Handbook of Marijuana* (New York: University Books, 1967), pp. 81-82.

17. *Ibid.*, p. 97.

18. *Ibid.*, pp. 86-87.

19. Edward R. Bloomquist, "Marijuana: Social benefit or social detriment?" *Calif. Med.,* 106:346-353 (May, 1967).

20. Earl Wilson, "The Crazy Dreamers," *Colliers Magazine,* July 4, 1949.

21. *Ibid.*

22. Charles W. Wahl, "The Diagnosis and Treatment of Status Medicamentosus," Drug Takers Symposium, University of California, Los Angeles, 1967.

COCHRAN

"No pot for me, thanks. I'll just get drunk like the
good Lord intended me to."

THE MAJOR CONTROVERSIES 5

> *Be calm in arguing; for fierceness makes*
> *Error a fault and truth a discourtesy*
>
> —George Herbert

We have looked at the facts: Cannabis is a weed with psychotoxic properties in its resin. For some 3,000 years, men of various cultures have used it to heighten perception and release inhibitions. It has been a religious sacrament in the East, a control-release mechanism for organized large-scale assassination in Arab countries, and is now a rallying cry of the psychedelic movement and the turned-on generation. In this latter role cannabis has sparked widespread controversy in the United States. It is indeed the controversy that interests most people, whichever side they take on it, and it is the controversy that will engage our attention in this chapter.

The arguments raised for and against cannabis are legion. Many of the specific questions are taken up in the appendix question-and-answer section. But the major questions reduce themselves to four, each. having to do with the relation of cannabis to, or comparison of cannabis with, some other area of activity. The four are: the cannabis-alcohol comparison, the cannabis-tobacco comparison, the relation of cannabis to crime, and the relation of cannabis to violence. Let us look at each in turn.

CANNABIS AND ALCOHOL

The argument is clear: From the standpoint of *physical* harm cannabis is not as bad as alcohol. *Psychologically* they are equally capable of producing erratic behavior and dependence.

Alcohol is legal. Why isn't cannabis?

The most eloquent proponent of the view that cannabis should be legal if alcohol is legal, is Indiana University Professor of Sociology Alfred R. Lindesmith. His book, *The Addict and the Law,* is a major document on the pro-cannabis side of the cannabis-alcohol debate. We will let Professor Lindesmith speak for the prosecution.[1]

"Investigators who rely on the opinions of high echelon officials, who have no direct acquaintance with the use of marijuana . . . usually reach the conclusion that marijuana is a highly dangerous drug which produces much violent crime and insanity," says Lindesmith. "These conclusions, as we have suggested, may be a reflection of upper-class hostility toward an unfamiliar lower-class indulgence."[2] For, he writes, "denunciations of the weed come characteristically from persons of those classes which prefer whiskey, rum, gin and other alcoholic beverages and who do not themselves use marijuana. Such persons, overlooking the well-known effects of alcohol, commonly deplore the effects of hemp upon the lower classes and often believe that it produces murder, rape, violence and insanity."[3]

He continues: "Ironically, the accusations that are leveled at marijuana are all applicable to alcohol, as has been demonstrated by innumerable investigations."[4] Lindesmith then goes on to list the many arguments against alcohol, then follows this with the observation that "the controversy with respect to marijuana is solely concerning the relative prevalence or frequency of such results in comparison to similar consequences following from the use of alcoholic beverages. All empirical investigations indicate that alcohol constitutes a far greater social danger than marijuana."[5]

Lindesmith maintains, "Intrinsically, however, marijuana is less dangerous and less harmful to the human body than is alcohol. It is, for example, not habit forming, where alcohol is. While the alcoholic commonly substitutes alcohol for food, marijuana sharply stimulates the appetite. . . . In comparison [to alcohol] the smoking of marijuana produces relatively trivial physical effects, although it does appear that immoderate use of the more concentrated products of the hemp plant also produces deleterious bodily effects. Such effects, however, are not conspicuous among American reefer smokers, probably because of the relatively small quantities of the essential drug that are ingested from the poor quality marijuana ordinarily consumed in this country. The American marijuana smoker who inadvertently uses too much when he switches, let us say, to the more potent ganja plant raised in Mexico and the West Indies is likely to experience nothing more alarming than going to sleep and waking up hungry."[6]

Lindesmith further argues that "marijuana has had no noticeable effect in increasing the population of our mental institutions, and whatever crimes of violence it may instigate are as nothing when compared to those that are linked with the use of alcohol."[7] He also argues that the accounts of the evils of marijuana are normally based on information about hashish. "The comparison of hashish and marijuana is like that between pure alcohol and beer. Lurid accounts of the psychological effects and dangers of hemp are often based upon observations made by and upon hashish users."[8] He even adds his mite to the praises sung to cannabis when he reports, "In Jamaica it is known to many persons of the lower classes as 'the wisdom weed' and it is alleged that it stimulates good qualities in the person who uses it and brings him closer to God. There, the use of ganja . . . is supported by references to various Biblical passages which recommend the 'herbs of the field.' "[9]

Finally, Lindesmith makes the grudging admission that marijuana may not be all good: "No one, of course, recommends the use of marihuana nor does anyone deny that there are evil effects and consequences associated with using it. The fact that the use of marihuana is outlawed, for example, means that it is often obtained through association with unsavory types, often used in an underworld environment, and the user takes the risk of criminal prosecution. *It is also undeniable that marihuana intoxication may sometimes lead to automobile accidents and to irresponsible or criminal acts*" [italics supplied].[10]

There are some obvious discrepancies in Lindesmith's own testimony on behalf of cannabis, most notably the last statement cited from him, but the burden of his argument must still be met. It is that opposition to cannabis is a matter of class or social prejudice and that cannabis is not as dangerous either to the individual or to society as alcohol. Let us reserve the alcohol argument for a moment and question the validity of the class-prejudice assertions.

If there ever was any substance to the interpretation of cannabis opposition on social or class lines, it has long since disappeared with the arrival of marijuana in the middle and upper-middle classes. Perhaps in the Thirties when marijuana use was almost exclusively associated with immigrant Mexicans, with Negroes, and with jazz musicians, there was some ground for Lindesmith's class approach. Today there is none. The most vociferous proponents and the most conspicuous users of cannabis today come from the very classes that Lindesmith claims have a built-in prejudice against marijuana for reasons of social station. Indeed, one of the most frequently encountered pro-cannabis arguments, especially from the young, is that many prominent and socially distinguished people use cannabis, so why shouldn't they? This argument is something close to an inversion of Lindesmith's claims, for marijuana today has a kind of social prestige because of its college and entertainment-world associations. It is, moreover, among the college youth, not among the laboring classes, that agitation is strongest for the legalization of marijuana. In short, Lindesmith's class argument is a red herring, however sincerely believed, which seems designed to cast marijuana users in the role of underdog and a socially oppressed minority endeavoring quietly to pursue their own pleasure while a combine of money and social position grinds its heels on the faces of the poor. The "connections" know better: they regularly work the campus and the college bars and restaurants; they will not be found outside the steel mill when the shifts change hoping to peddle their product.

Now, before turning to the more serious charge of cannabis and alcohol, let us look at the testimony of Dr. David Smith, Clinical Instructor in Pharmacology at the University of California and the mainstay of the Haight-Ashbury clinic in San Francisco for drug-using hippies. Dr. Smith is probably in closer contact with socially dissociated and drug-using youth than any other physician in the United States. He recently testified before a California State Assembly committee[11] that alcohol is as dangerous as marijuana and marijuana as dangerous as alcohol. Further, he noted that the alcohol argument had caused many young people to distrust all drug information given them by authorities, since they believe the authorities follow a double standard when it comes to alcohol versus cannabis. Some Haight-Ashbury users go so far as to suspect that recent releases on the chromosome destructive effects of LSD are nothing more than a government plot to keep them from enjoying their drug.

Dr. Smith noted that the use of drugs in the Hashbury is so widespread that 40 percent of the people he interviewed admitted they had swallowed pills without having any idea what they were. Ninety-five percent said they have used cannabis; ninety percent said they use it regularly. In this admittedly drug-oriented community 80 percent of the young people admitted that they were drinking alcohol when they arrived. After a time only 15 percent continued to drink it. The others considered it a dangerous drug. The group involved falls mainly between fifteen and twenty-five with a median age of twenty years. Those who continue to drink, and in many cases therefore violate the alcohol laws, are rarely arrested for this offense since police seem primarily interested in apprehending cannabis and other drug violators. Nevertheless, alcohol consumption is not an important part of the activity of the drug community in the Haight-Ashbury district.

According to Dr. Smith, the legality of alcohol versus the illegality of cannabis has created a hostile resentment among cannabis users. Many drug-using youths today consider themselves a minority that is being set upon by an establishment intent upon retaining alcohol and tobacco for themselves while denying the use of cannabis to others. This division may seem to be reminiscent of Lindesmith's class conflict, but the classes in question are quite different from his division. The lines here have much more to do with rebellion within a single large class. The middle- and upper-middle class backgrounds of the Haight-Ashbury drug community are well documented. The members of it are more often than not rebelling against their own parents and backgrounds, not against an alien social class.

But the important point that can be taken from both Lindesmith and Smith is that, first, many believe a double standard exists in the defense of alcohol coupled with an attack on marijuana, and that, secondly, the conviction that alcohol is as bad or worse than marijuana provides one of the main intellectual arguments of the drug world in favor of continued use and eventual legalization of cannabis. This is the nub of the cannabis-alcohol debate.

First of all, let us concede there are many horrors associated with alcohol. There are endless statistics that document them. Seventy million Americans drink regularly; six million or more are alcoholics. One out of three arrests is for drunkenness; one out of four male admissions to mental hospitals is for alcoholism.[12] The chance of meeting a drunken driver on the road is present in one out of every ten cars you pass, and the National Safety Council estimates that liquor-caused property damage on the highways amounted to four billion dollars in 1966. There were 29,400 people killed in alcohol-related auto accidents in 1965. Alcohol-associated absenteeism costs industry over two billion dollars a year. Finally, 75 percent of the domestic-relations actions brought into court have alcoholism as one of the contributing factors.

Alcohol is a narcotic drug; not an opiate but a narcotic. So it is defined in the dictionary. It is a classic drug of addiction, producing psychological dependence, tolerance, physical dependence, and acute withdrawal symptoms in the addicted.

All these things are facts. To deny or distort them is to confirm the charges of hypocrisy and double-dealing so often made by the pro-cannabis forces. But what does *not* automatically follow from these facts is that alcohol constitutes a greater social danger than marijuana, or that the general comparison of alcohol and marijuana is meaningful and logically compelling.

As attorney Donald Miller recently wrote:

> It has become popular with those who would legalize marijuana to claim that its use is no worse than the current use of alcohol. However, any comparison of marijuana with other substances such as alcohol is extremely tenuous at best and, in a basic sense, such efforts are pointless. The attempt, no matter how successful, can produce no guide to action. Surely it is not valid to justify the adoption of a new vice by

trying to show that it is no worse than a presently existing one. It is true that alcohol abuse also constitutes a major social problem, but the social damage which would result from a permissive use of marijuana cannot, like some finely balanced equation, be canceled out by placing a measure of social damage resulting from alcohol opposite it. The result can only be additive.[13]

Mr. Miller states the case succinctly. It is a fallacy to suggest that the existence of one evil excuses or encourages the establishment of another. Indeed, the existence of alcoholism and of skid rows is not an argument in *favor* of cannabis but one against it. If alcohol has ruined six million lives in this country how can it possibly be an argument for permitting cannabis to do the same, or worse? Logic compels those who argue against alcohol to excuse cannabis to take another stand: they should be arguing for the control of alcohol and the elimination of its evils, not for the extension of those or similar evils to a wider segment of society.

We need not anticipate a sudden upsurge in the membership of the WCTU by reform-minded hippies, because the real reason for the drug community's alcohol attack and comparison has nothing to do with concern for alcoholism or its evils. It is a case of special pleading and question-begging. The attack on alcohol implicitly acknowledges the evils of cannabis and goes on to urge that we let two wrongs make a right. The fact is that alcoholism is a different problem with an entirely different ethos and history. What to do about alcoholism cannot be discussed here, but we should be clear that legalization of cannabis will in no way alleviate the problems of alcoholism but is very likely to add problems of another sort.

It is an interesting fact that alcohol and cannabis have rarely coexisted in the same culture. In the East, where alcohol has long been frowned upon or outlawed, cannabis has been a religious sacrament. In the West alcohol, in the form of sacramental wine, has been tied with religious activities. Cannabis has always been alien to the Judeo-Christian world. In this sense our society has been opposed to the use of cannabis, often without realizing why, on purely religious grounds.

H. B. Murphy makes another point as to why cannabis is

so regularly banned in countries where alcohol is permitted. One of the reasons, he feels, is the positive value placed on action and the hostility toward passivity. "In Anglo-Saxon cultures," Murphy says,

> inaction is looked down on and often feared, whereas over-activity, aided by alcohol or independent of alcohol, is considerably tolerated despite the social disturbance produced. It may be that we can ban cannabis simply because the people who use it, or would do so, carry little weight in social matters and are relatively easy to control; whereas the alcohol user often carries plenty of weight in social matters and is difficult to control, as the United States prohibition era showed. It has yet to be shown, however, that the one is more socially or personally disruptive than the other.[14]

Murphy's final statement is, of course, largely true and has not been denied in this study, but perhaps it should more properly be phrased to induce the recognition that one drug is *as* socially and personally disruptive as the other. The question is whether we, as a nation, can afford a second drug catastrophe. If we had never known the effects of alcohol it would have been reasonably simple to enforce the Eighteenth Amendment (the Volstead Act). But we were fully aware of its effects long before Americans became upset about alcoholism, just as people in the East were aware of cannabis long before the present restrictive laws were passed outlawing cannabis use in any major country in the world. One can expect, therefore, that enforcement of these anti-cannabis laws in the Orient will meet with the same resistance that prohibition met with in the United States.

As Ferdinand Mount recently noted, "If alcohol came to us as a new and untried drug with documented evidence from say, France, of consequent DT's, cirrhosis, habituation, and bar-room violence as well as the conviviality, release from inhibitions and cheerful distortions of perceptions resulting from its use, would responsible ministers and educators blithely urge its legalization?"[15]

Finally, something more should be said about the comparison of alcohol to cannabis. Without defending alcohol and without granting the aptness of the alcohol-cannabis comparison, let us note some important points. The overall actions of cannabis are such that they make the user more dangerous when he approaches the toxic level than the alcoholic who is equally "high." The alcoholic goes through a period on his way to becoming drunk during which he is indeed a menace to public safety, as evidenced by the number of traffic accidents. At the high danger point, however, one who is drunk either recognizes that he is incapacitated or simply passes out. The pattern is not the same for a cannabis user. Whereas a user of alcohol may enjoy his vice without getting high, a user of cannabis *must* get high to enjoy it. The point may be debated, but as the American Medical Association points out: "Most persons usually do not take alcohol to the point of intoxication. One or two drinks a day normally have little effect. On the other hand, one or two reefers can produce marihuana intoxication."[16]

Most critical of all, as the drunk gets drunker and finally collapses, the cannabis user becomes more toxic and active. He is not reduced to incoordination to the point of immobility but rather only to the point of endangering himself and others. As toxicity increases hallucinations appear and feelings of great strength and capability, usually unwarranted, begin to take over. Soon the cannabis user thinks he can walk on water, jump over buildings, or walk between the headlights of an oncoming car. Less dangerous than alcohol?

Again, we are not excusing alcohol. Nor should we forget that the comparison argument is disingenuous at best and certainly not logically compelling. But since the comparison will repeatedly be made it is important to bear in mind that, similar as some of the effects of alcohol and cannabis are, there are these others, just cited, that are quite dissimilar indeed. They do not strengthen the case for cannabis. Let us also finally bear in mind that we have abundant evidence on the effects of alcohol and that we know with something like certainty the full range of these effects. Such is not the case with cannabis. What evidence we have in the United States, and it is grim enough, is based on the use of relatively mild forms of cannabis. There is no warrant to assume, if the cannabis habit spreads through legalization or other means, that the only types of cannabis that will be used are mexicana and, occasionally, americana. There is every reason to suppose that there would be a special premium on *Cannabis indica,* much as there is on the more potent forms of alcohol. So far, we have been in the beer and wine stage of cannabis use. The whiskey stage is likely to prove even more disturbing.

We leave the cannabis-alcohol comparison, since society has thus far seen fit to legalize the use of alcohol, with the advice of Omar Khayyám: "Waste not your hour now in the vain pursuit of this and that endeavor and dispute. Better be jocund with the fruitful grape than sadder after none or bitter fruit."[17]

CANNABIS AND TOBACCO

The comparison between cannabis and tobacco is often made by the pro-cannabis people for the same reasons the alcohol comparison is made. Many of the same rebuttals apply.

The pro-cannabis case is put by writer Antoni Gollan: "There is growing speculation within medical circles that cannabis may be no more dangerous than tobacco or liquor. These two substances are widely used in the United States." He continues: "We smoke, many of us, cigarettes conveniently packaged by R. J. Reynolds, P. Lorillard and the gang. We continue to inhale nicotine fumes despite the reported cancerous malignancies, destruction of lung cells, heart disease —despite evidence that smoking may interrupt life, and cancel the added years offered by the last half-century of medical science."

Gollan also points to the quasi-addictive nature of tobacco. "Smokers," he says, "develop psychological dependence on, and mild physical addiction to cigarettes. Ever try to quit smoking? The ordeal demands rigid self-discipline, and the withdrawal symptoms are nervousness and irritability."[18] But the chances of outlawing smoking, Gollan believes, are slim. He quotes U.S. Surgeon General Dr. William H. Stewart: "With forty percent of the population smoking, I don't think the public would stand up for a ban. We had one experience with Prohibition and I think it would, based on that experience, have the same kind of result."[19]

Now, again it is necessary to speak plainly about tobacco. It is a problem, although of a quite different nature from cannabis. Senator Robert F. Kennedy, speaking to the World Conference on Smoking and Health of September 11, 1967, delivered himself of a mass of statistics about the evils of tobacco. Some of them are these: over a quarter of a million premature deaths each year are attributed to diseases associated with cigarette smoking; one-third of all male deaths between the ages of thirty-five and sixty come from diseases associated with cigarette smoking. Eleven million other persons have chronic diseases in the cigarette-smoking population. Death from lung cancer is increasing almost geometrically—from about 2,500 in 1930, shortly after smoking started becoming a national habit, to 50,000 today. If present rates continue one-seventh of all Americans now alive—about twenty-eight million people—will die prematurely of diseases associated with cigarette smoking.

And there are many more statistics of the same sort. Senator Kennedy asserted that cigarettes would long since have been banned were it not for the power of the tobacco industry. He said: "If the cigarette industry's economic power were as miniscule as that of the marijuana industry, cigarettes would surely be illegal now and their sale subject to severe penalty as a health hazard." He concluded: "The cigarette companies have demonstrated a total inattention to public responsibility. But it is also a reflection on our society, on all of us, that cigarette smoking has been permitted to continue in our various countries. There is no reason for another generation of mankind to end up disabled and the victim of premature death. We must act and act now."[20]

It should be clear, as it should have been in the case of alcohol, that not all of the establishment has a special interest in maintaining a privileged status for tobacco. But more important it should be clear that the evil effects of tobacco do not excuse the use of marijuana. The same illogic that couples alcohol abuse with an appeal to legalize marijuana is operating in the case of tobacco, although the links are even more tenuous and the parallels more farfetched.

The ill effects of tobacco use are primarily medical, those of cannabis primarily social, although cannabis enjoys the distinction of having certain medical ill effects as well. Apart from the fact that most cannabis used in the United States is smoked, there is little connection between marijuana and tobacco. Nor can one discern any serious interest among the pro-cannabis apologists for the banning of tobacco, which is the field they ought to be working in if their concern is truly for the deleterious effects of smoking. Rather, the pro-cannabis spokesmen have seized upon one abuse as the grounds for condoning another. As with alcohol, the effect will not be a cancelling out of abuses but the multiplication of them.

Even though the argument fails for lack of relevance, it will continue to be heard. For that reason bear in mind the following facts that arise out of the comparison of cannabis and tobacco. The tobacco smoker may suffer a lethal influence on his physical health; the cannabis smoker may suffer an insidious devastation of his mind and the development of an amotivational syndrome. Further, there is no acute intoxication with tobacco; the effects are cumulative and ultimately chronic. Cannabis, however, presents an acute toxicity syndrome that manifests its results both immediately and cumulatively.

The argument sometimes encountered that smoking cigarettes leads to the use of marijuana is a very weak argument indeed and probably most often represents a grasping at straws by the person making it. Certainly the associations and motivations of tobacco smokers and marijuana smokers are quite different as are also most of the effects of the two. As Max Miller has pointed out in his excellent film "Marijuana," no one has ever dropped out of school because of his addiction to tobacco; no one who just smoked a cigarette ever forgot he was driving a car and began tripping on a cloud or a flashing light in the distance; and no cigarette salesman ever tried to induce a buyer to take up the heroin needle. Further, as Miller notes, one can smoke cigarettes and do many other useful and productive things even while smoking. Marijuana, however, absorbs the full time and attention of the user at, least while he is using, and sometimes it repeats on him when he is not using.[21] In this connection it has sometimes been claimed that subsequent tobacco use precipitates a previous cannabis experience, just as cannabis use can precipitate a previous drug experience from LSD or from cannabis itself. Once again, the problem is with the previous use of the hallucinogen, not with the tobacco.

Fundamentally, the two problems, tobacco and cannabis use, are different not in degree but in kind. It clouds the issue of cannabis use to introduce such a poorly related issue as tobacco. Those who do are darkening counsel, usually to gain the tactical advantage of obliging one's enemy to go on the defensive. But, as was clear with alcohol, all the ills ever ascribed to tobacco will not persuade thoughtful people to accept new and more perilous hazards associated with the use of cannabis.

CANNABIS AND CRIME

At this point the initiative is taken by the anti-cannabis forces. The arguments relating to alcohol and tobacco are essentially pro-cannabis arguments designed to excuse one evil on the grounds of the existence of others. The arguments relating to cannabis and crime, and cannabis and violence, which is discussed later, are essentially anti-cannabis arguments designed to strengthen the case against cannabis because of its unsavory associations. Both sets of arguments, then, pro- and anti-cannabis, are forms of guilt (or innocence) by association, with all of the dangers implicit in such argumentation. In the case of cannabis vis-a-vis liquor and tobacco we have seen that innocence by association is not in fact proven at all, that actually the pro-cannabis spokesmen virtually admit that cannabis is undesirable and either rest content with saying, "so are alcohol and tobacco," or seek to take the offensive and argue that the existence of other evils excuses this one. We must be just as searching in our examination of the anti-cannabis arguments regarding crime and violence.

First the crime argument. Does the use of cannabis cause a person to become a criminal? To be quite clear, let us exclude from the definition of criminality in this instance the violation of anti-cannabis laws. Although such violation is criminal in the United States, the charge of criminality as it relates to the argument of cannabis association has to do with crimes of violence—murder, rape, assault—and with theft. Let us also ask what is meant by "cause." Direct causal relationships are very hard to prove. We must ask in every case whether a crime was clearly *caused* by cannabis, and then we must ask in general whether the association between cannabis and crime is sufficiently frequent and widespread to justify general statements about a causal relationship between the drug and crime.

Attorney Gene Haislip has argued that criminal activity can be stimulated by cannabis in several ways: (1) by being used by certain criminals to fortify their courage prior to committing crimes; (2) by causing crimes to occur because of a general mental derangement and demoralization after chronic use of cannabis (usually hashish); (3) by precipitating criminal behavior because marginally adjusted persons lower their inhibitions and thus stimulate aggressive and antisocial tendencies; and (4) by causing crimes resulting from panic, confusion, or anger induced in otherwise normal persons who react adversely to the drug's effects.[22]

It is difficult to tell how many persons actually indulge in crime either aided or caused by the use of cannabis. Police files are full of such cases; yet one must always question whether or not the use of the drug was an *adjunct* rather than the *cause* of the problem. Police and law enforcement authorities generally take the hard line that there is a causal relationship between marijuana and crime and that the two are in any case very frequently associated.

Inspector Burnell Blanchard of the California Attorney General's Bureau of Narcotic Enforcement argues insistently that the connection between cannabis and crime is not coincidental. Ten years ago Blanchard was involved in the case of an East Los Angeles gang that set fires by tossing Molotov cocktails indiscriminately at residences and business establishments. When the gang was broken up police learned that the gang leader, known as "Duke," had drawn up elaborate plans to set a spectacular holocaust to totally destroy Los Angeles County General Hospital. The connection with cannabis was this: Duke and his gang regularly became intoxicated with marijuana before their raids. It stilled the inhibitions of those members who were not sadistically violent and enabled them to carry out Duke's orders without qualms. Further, it intensified for them the exciting sensations of noise, sirens, burning fires, and general chaos that surrounded the blazes they set.

Such encounters with cannabis are extremely frequent in

police work. When the police hear that "only a few" users become involved with crime they wonder how they keep meeting that few so constantly. And in truth there is a considerable gap between the experiences of the sociologist in his university office, or the psychiatrist in his handsomely appointed quarters on the one hand, and the police on the street on the other. It may not be so much that one or the other is wrong as that they just move in different circles.

Let us look at those circles familiar to the psychiatrist and sociologist to see what their findings are in regard to cannabis and crime. Socio-psychiatrist Joel Fort says blandly that "cannabis is a valuable pleasure-giving drug, probably much safer than alcohol."[23] Pharmacologist Frederick Meyers recently told the California State Assembly on Public Health that "it must be acknowledged that the brief duration of action and low potency of available marijuana preparations, and its freedom from the nutritional side effects of alcohol, do indeed suggest a lesser hazard in the use of marijuana."[24] Ausubel in 1958 said that a fair summary of the available evidence "would be that very rarely do major crimes follow upon the use of [cannabis] and that, in instances where they do, the relationship is an indirect one."[25] Earlier, in 1945, Gaskill contended that "marihuana like alcohol does not necessarily produce abnormal behavior. The danger lies in the fact that immature and psychopathic persons use it to deaden their perception of reality, and when under its effects their inhibitions and judgement are impaired with consequent increase in abnormal behavior. . . . [Cannabis may act] as the determining factor turning the balance in the direction of asocial behavior rather than permitting the poorly integrated social conscience of such an individual to remain in control."[26]

Ausubel does concede that, in addition to releasing latent criminally associated trends, cannabis may contribute to premeditated crime when used to bolster courage prior to the act, such as described by Blanchard in the case of "Duke" and his gang, or as was done on a large scale by Hasan-Ibn-Sabbah. Ausubel also notes, "Some of the more sensational instances of homicide and sexual assault attributed to marijuana intoxication are undoubtedly manifestations of transitory psychotic states induced by the drug." But he also says that "still another reason for the association of marijuana addiction and crime is the greater use of marijuana in slum-urban areas where delinquency rates tend to be high." In view of the variety of responses to cannabis, Ausubel is also obliged to note that "marijuana, by virtue of its stupefying effects, may sometimes inhibit the expression of aggressive impulses."[27]

Thus even the best authorities find it difficult to be conclusive in their view of the relationship between cannabis and crime.

Much more positive, and much more permissive, is the voice of the distinguished psychiatrist Lawrence Kolb. In 1962 Kolb noted that, while the crime-producing properties of marijuana had been carefully studied in at least five investigations by competent scientists in America, no association between cannabis and aggressive crime was discovered in any of these studies, nor did any of the investigators conclude that such a thing as a marijuana-induced murder ever occurred.[28]

Kolb has argued against many aspects of the anti-marijuana laws expressing the idea that marijuana has been grossly overrated as a harmful drug. "Marihuana, like alcohol," he says, "releases the user's inhibitions and distorts his judgment. When used excessively, it may cause criminally-inclined persons to commit crimes, but its potency as an instigator of crime has not been measured or demonstrated in the United States because of its limited use."[29]

"The tendency," Kolb complains, "to credit a narcotic as the cause of physical, mental and social disasters is so great in the United States that marihuana-induced crimes are often reported in the press and by police-trained people when there is no causal relation of marihuana to the crime." To support this contention he cites the case of two young men who had drunk some whiskey in a hotel room, then smoked a marijuana cigarette, then quarreled, and fought. One killed the other. The story, says Kolb, was played up in the press as a vicious marijuana-induced murder.[30] Kolb's story points up some of the dangers in relying solely on police reporters for facts about criminality. But it is also true that the journalistic climate has changed since Kolb wrote in 1962, and the tendency today is not toward sensationalized crime reporting so much as a scarcely veiled journalistic thrill in covering the fashionable aspects of marijuana.

Kolb also argued that the reason we have so little data on marijuana and crime is the miniscule number of marijuana users, especially as contrasted with alcohol users. The situation is considerably different today, but crime attorney Donald E. Miller points out that there has long been more evidence than Kolb allowed.[31] A 1939 study by Dr. Walter Bromberg in New Orleans—where marijuana first was used extensively in this country—showed that the number of marijuana users among major criminals was very high.[32] In other countries the evidence is even greater. In the article "Marihuana and Crime" James Munch cites at least twenty-eight articles in scientific journals between 1908 and 1964 which reported close association between cannabis use and morbid crime.[33]

Munch noted that I. C. and R. N. Chopra "made a study of 1500 cases of whom 600 in a mental hospital had been using cannabis. A substantial proportion were also arrested for crime. Fossier reported that 125 of 450 prisoners in New Orleans were marijuana addicts, at ages between 18 and 31. One-fourth of the total prisoners arrested were addicted to marijuana and he reached the conclusion 'marijuana is a real menace to the community.' Similar observations were reported by Lambo," Munch says, "and others."

We ought to take a brief look at Lambo's report.[34] Lambo is a West African psychiatrist and physician at the University of Ibadan in Nigeria. He reports that in West Africa the commonly used drug is cannabis (hashish in this case). He found that the first users of cannabis in Nigeria, just as in the United States today, were high school and college students. More than half of the cases he studied came to his attention before they had reached the age of twenty-five. Each one had a cannabis-use history of from three to five years. The reasons for use were very similar to those that prevail in the United States, and there was a striking difference in personality patterns between those who used cannabis and those who did not. A special psychiatric study by Lambo of 434 of the users revealed that more than 60 percent had severe behavior disorders. Their basic psychopathology was one of a chronic feeling of inadequacy, frustration, and anxiety. The longer they used the drug the more they demonstrated a general failure of personality integration. The more poorly integrated they were into life situations the more likely they were to turn to cannabis.

Lambo said that the drug does not always produce permanent disturbance of personality but in some cases it does give rise to an impairment of mental health. In schoolboys there were consistent gross emotional and other behavioral difficulties. One feature he encountered again and again was a complete lack of understanding on the part of the users of the problems their behavior might cause.

The relationship of crime and antisocial behavior to cannabis, Lambo says, is a most complex and elusive problem. Even so he found a very strong association between crime and offenses in which cannabis was involved. In fact, cannabis-associated crimes ranked fourth on a list compiled by Lambo. Of seventy-three murders that occurred in three West African nations, 51 percent had been committed by cannabis users. Thirty-one percent of assault and battery cases had been committed by cannabis users. Approximately 78 percent of all burglaries were performed by cannabis users. Moreover, Lambo claimed that the association between crime and cannabis in West Africa seems to be steadily mounting. He believes the reason is that cannabis produces a temporary feeling of well-being and blunts critical judgment and releases inhibitions. Further, its use has spread from youth and students to domestic servants, migrant workers, soldiers, truck drivers, factory workers, and professionals. It has become a national health problem. How far it went in one of these nations, Nigeria, will be discussed later.

Observations by the Chopras in India when cannabis was legal prompted them to observe: "Excessive indulgence in cannabis is apt to produce in healthy individuals and more so in susceptible individuals, mental confusion which may lead to delusions with restlessness and disordered movements. Intellectual impairment as well as disorientation may show itself in various ways, such as weakening of the moral sense, habit of telling lies, prostitution, theft, pilfering, sex perversions and other disgraceful practices. Sometimes indulgence may release subconscious impulses and lead to violent crimes."[35]

The Chopras findings, of course, relate to Indian hashish users, not users of mild American marijuana, and they date from 1957. Thirteen years earlier a commission in America studying American cannabis users wrote in the LaGuardia Report: ". . . there were alterations in behavior giving rise to antisocial expression. This was shown by unconventional acts not permitted in public, anxiety reactions, opposition and antagonism, and eroticism. Effects such as these would be conducive to acts of violence." Later in the report the committee also wrote: "The conclusion seems warranted that given the potential make-up and the right time and environment, marijuana may bring on a true psychotic state."[36]

There is, then, testimony from informed persons on both sides of the cannabis-crime question. But the issue does not end simply in a toss-up. What seems clear is that cannabis *per se* does not cause crime, in the sense that anyone taking it will of necessity commit criminal acts. But what is just as clear is that cannabis releases inhibitions and impairs judgment with such regular predictability that a user with criminal tendencies will readily commit crimes under the influence of cannabis. And it is documented that many already confirmed criminals use cannabis to buoy them up for the commission of criminal acts. The intent, or at least the disposition, to engage in criminal activity must exist in the user before using cannabis. But there seems to be a high incidence of what, at best, we must call unstable personalities who are attracted to cannabis, and the combination no doubt results in the frequently high correlation that law enforcement authorities have noted between cannabis and crime.

CANNABIS AND VIOLENCE

This issue is very closely related to the issue of cannabis and violence, largely because our knowledge of most violent acts comes from police statistics and law enforcement information. The difference between the two questions—cannabis and crime and cannabis and violence—is chiefly one of emphasis.

The question of violence has more to do with whether physical injury is inflicted on other persons than with whether a cannabis user is engaging in such criminal acts as theft, arson, prostitution, or acts directed against society at large. Nevertheless, there is obviously a good deal of overlap.

The case for the connection between cannabis and violence or violent crime is again one made by the anti-cannabis forces. Here again the police and law enforcement authorities provide the information. They base their charges on the many documented criminal cases where marijuana was a factor. To indicate the nature of police charges, let us look at some typical cases as they came from the files of the Los Angeles Police Department, compiled in 1966 in a special survey of the relationship between marijuana and criminal behavior. The cases presented are but a fraction of the hundreds compiled by the L.A.P.D.

Case 1

Officers received a call regarding a family dispute. The officers were met by the suspect's wife who stated that she and her husband had had an argument and she had threatened to leave with the children. The suspect became violent and struck her several times in the face. When she fell down, he kicked her several times in the ribs. The suspect then dragged the victim to a staircase and pushed her down the stairs. Officers could smell the odor of marijuana coming from within the house in which the suspect had locked himself. After entry was made and the suspect arrested, officers found in the suspect's bedroom a quantity of Zig-zag paper and a pipe filled with marijuana.

Case 2

A victim reported to the police that she had been kidnapped and robbed during the early morning hours. She stated that a man had held a knife at her throat and forced her into his car. The suspect then tried to force the victim to smoke a marijuana cigarette but she refused. The suspect then removed $30 from the victim's purse and forced her out of the car. The arresting officers located the suspect's apartment and at the time of the arrest officers found a partially smoked marijuana cigarette in an ashtray and a large bag of marijuana in a closet.

Case 3

A landlady of an apartment house reported that one of her female tenants had fired two shots at her. The officers went to the suspect's apartment and, after knocking and identifying themselves, the door was opened and the suspect pointed a .25 automatic pistol at them. Upon disarming the female the officers heard the toilet flush and, upon entering the bathroom, observed the defendant's boyfriend attempting to dispose of a quantity of marijuana. When the female suspect was being booked, officers found two plastic bags containing marijuana in her purse.

Case 4

Radio car officers received a call regarding a disturbance at an apartment house. Upon their arrival the manager related that a man had run up the stairs with a bumper jack in his hand and had entered an apartment. When the officers reached the apartment, they could hear a female inside screaming, "Don't kill me, George, please don't kill me." The officers knocked on the door and identified themselves and the female cried, "Oh God, please come in, he's killing me." The officers forcibly entered and observed the suspect standing over the victim with the jack handle over his head poised to strike. The suspect was taken into custody and a marijuana cigarette was found in his pocket. The suspect stated he had smoked at least four marijuana cigarettes that day.

Case 5

Officers received a radio call: "woman screaming." When they arrived the officers were met by a man and a woman, each claiming he was the victim of assault by the other. Both parties showed evidence of injury. The female suspect stated "I smoked two or three roaches. He looked at me with a weird look in his eye and called me a profanity. I picked up the ice pick and hit him with it. I am high now." It was noted that the male had been stabbed three times. A search of the house disclosed marijuana debris in several ashtrays.

Case 6

Radio car officers answered a call to a playground regarding an assault suspect. The officers were told by the playground director that he had ordered the sixteen-year-old subject from the athletic field because of a disturbance he was causing. The playground director suspected the youngster was intoxicated because his voice was slurred, his eyes partially shut, and he was staggering. The subject had also become antagonistic, swore, and swung his fists at the director. Marijuana debris was found in the subject's pocket and he then admitted he had smoked three marijuana cigarettes just prior to the altercation.

Case 7

Officers received a radio call that shots had been fired. Upon investigation it was discovered that the suspect had earlier been ejected from a bar for a disturbance. Fifteen minutes later he returned and fired several shots from a shotgun in the street outside the bar. When the patrons of the bar quickly emptied into the street, the suspect fired in their direction striking one in the leg. Numerous shotguns, rifles, and pistols were found in the suspect's home. In the closet was found a large quantity of marijuana. The suspect admitted smoking marijuana that day and on numerous previous occasions.

Now, the argument in all of these cases is similar to that already examined in the cannabis-crime discussion. One extra factor that must be considered in judging these cases is that users of cannabis may develop a toxic psychosis from high concentrations of the drug and in this psychotic state become violent because of their inability to control hostile, paranoid, and sometimes, homicidal trends. Whether or not this factor was present in any of the previously reported cases or in other cases that might be considered must be decided by critical evaluation of each individual incident. In a few cases it may well be that violence is the result of a drug-induced psychotic state. In most cases of cannabis use in the United States, however, it is unlikely that the drug actually *caused* the reported violence. Conversely, however, it is quite likely that it *facilitated* it.

In the final analysis, says attorney Gene Haislip,[37] the question is not in what manner cannabis caused the violence or the crime. Instead it is sociologically important to determine how many, if any, of the crimes would not have been committed if the individual had not been using cannabis at the time of the incident. Pro-cannabis forces demand more direct proof of crime or violence caused by cannabis than cases merely showing their frequent association can provide. In regard to such demands for "proof," Los Angeles surgeon William F. Quinn recently stated: "If I had to have all the statistics and reports you people need to make your decisions in order to arrive at a diagnosis, most of my patients would die of a ruptured appendix." Smiling at his audience of sociologists and psychiatrists, Dr. Quinn then added, "Fortunately for sick people, surgeons are more practical than that."[38]

To turn to the pro-cannabis replies of the association of cannabis violence, let us consider the testimony of author-student Stephen Abrams. He writes: "Another criticism that is frequently made is that cannabis tends to cause violence and crime. . . . I find this extremely difficult to believe." He observed a group of cannabis users at Oxford University and found no evidence of violence: "During the so-called 'crisis' the most violent activity that is likely to occur is uninhibited dancing. I have observed hundreds of persons under the influence of cannabis and have never seen a single act of violence committed."[39]

As in the case of some psychiatrists and sociologists, Abrams appears to move in different circles than the police. One man's observations are, in any case, hardly sufficient to generalize about the vast drug picture today; but it must also be borne in mind that Abrams and many other pro-cannabis commentators are confined in their observations to the college crowd, while many who are attracted to cannabis do not fall in the category of Oxford University undergraduates. In fact, the usage of cannabis, according to the American Medical Association, is "probably disproportionately higher among young persons with developing psychiatric problems than among those without them. Persons who use marijuana continually and as the symptomatic expression of psychological conflict, a means of gaining social acceptance, or a way of escaping painful experiences of anxiety or depression may be said to be psychological dependent upon the substance. Continuous use may be associated with the development of psychiatric illness, although few chronic users are admitted to psychiatric inpatient facilities." The AMA warns further: "It is likely that those who do become dependent on marijuana or other drugs are psychiatrically disturbed, and that drug use is but one of a complex of psychological and behavioral symptoms manifested by them."[40]

Now, let us review again what cannabis does to the mind: Release of inhibitions, distortion of perception and judgment, increased response to suggestion, production in susceptible people of illusions and delusions that predispose to antisocial behavior, impairment of memory, distortion of emotional responsiveness, irritability and confusion and a predisposition to anxiety and aggressiveness as a possible result of various intellectual and sensory derangements. That particular catalog comes from the 1965 report of the Committee on Drug Dependence of the World Health Organization.

However much we qualify allegations about the relationship between cannabis and violence or crime, no amount of qualification can obscure the fact that marijuana can produce psychotic reactions (this is a simple medical fact) and that a psychotic state can release violence and precipitate criminal behavior. This is not to say that it will in every case but that it can and has. Because of the relative mildness of Mexican and American varieties of cannabis we have seen very little of this kind of cannabis-induced reaction. But with the coming of more potent oriental varieties, with the coming of hashish, we can look for more and more instances of psychosis and violence as a result of cannabis use.

Obviously the connection between cannabis and violence or crime depends most of all on the individual user and, secondarily, on who is examining and evaluating his behavior. If the user is not prone to violence or crime and if he does not develop a drug-induced psychosis he will not, except for the infraction of the narcotics laws, normally resort to violent or criminal behavior. If, on the other hand, he is one of those who are predisposed to antisocial behavior and violence, any-

102

thing may happen when he is taking marijuana. This is the issue in determining whether to legalize cannabis or not. Considering that violence lies bubbling beneath the surface in many people, and especially in many who are attracted to cannabis, we must ask ourselves whether society wants to legalize a substance that releases personal restraints and inhibitions as one of its most reliable effects.

1. Alfred R. Lindesmith, *The Addict and the Law* (Bloomington: Indiana University Press, 1965).

2. *Ibid.*, p. 235.

3. *Ibid.*, p. 226.

4. *Ibid.*, p. 227.

5. *Ibid.*, p. 234.

6. *Ibid.*, p. 223.

7. *Ibid.*, p. 225.

8. *Ibid.*, p. 224.

9. *Ibid.*, p. 224.

10. *Ibid.*, p. 234.

11. David Smith, M.D., testimony given before California Assemblyman Pete Wilson, March 1, 1968, Los Angeles, California.

12. "A Little Family Cheer," *Newsweek,* Oct. 23, 1967.

13. Donald E. Miller, "Narcotic Drug and Marijuana Controls," paper presented at the National Association of Student Personnel Administrators Drug Education Conference, Washington, D.C., Nov. 7-8, 1966.

14. H. B. Murphy, "The cannabis habit: A review of recent psychiatric literature," *Bull. Narc.,* 15:1 (1963).

15. Ferdinand Mount, "The Wild Grass Chase," *National Review,* Jan. 20, 1968, p. 84.

16. *The Crutch that Cripples,* (Chicago: American Medical Association, 1967), p. 19.

17. Omar Khayyám. *Rubaiyat.*

18. Antoni Gollan, "The Great Marijuana Problem," *National Review,* Jan. 20, 1968, p. 75.

19. Dr. William H. Stewart, quoted in *ibid.*

20. Robert F. Kennedy, remarks before the World Conference on Smoking and Health, New York City, Sept. 11, 1967.

21. Max Miller, *Marijuana,* produced by Avanti Films, Los Angeles, 1968.

22. Gene R. Haislip, "Current Issues in the Prevention and

Control of Marijuana Abuse," paper presented to the First National Conference on Student Drug Involvement, University of Maryland, Aug. 16, 1967.

23. Joel Fort, quoted by Stephen Abrams, in "The Oxford Scene and the Law," in *The Book of Grass,* edited by George Andrews (New York: Grove Press, 1967), p. 235.

24. Frederick H. Meyers, comments in the Annual Report, Drug Abuse Information Project, University of California, Berkeley, California, Jan. 10, 1968.

25. David P. Ausubel, *Drug Addiction: Physiological, Psychological and Sociological Aspects,* (New York: Random House, 1964), p. 103.

26. H. S. Gaskill, "Marijuana, an intoxicant," *Amer. J. Psychiat.,* 102:202 (1945).

27. Ausubel, *op. cit.,* p. 104.

28. Lawrence Kolb, *Drug Addiction: A Medical Problem,* Springfield, Ill.: C. C Thomas, 1962, p. 24.

29. *Ibid.,* p. 23.

30. *Ibid.,* p. 23-24.

31. Donald E. Miller, *op. cit.*

32. Walter Bromberg, "Marijuana: A psychiatric study," *J.A.M.A.,* 113:4-12 (July, 1939).

33. James C. Munch, "Marijuana and Crime," INEOA 6th Annual Conference Report, pp. 55-61.

34. T. A. Lambo, "Medical and social problems of drug addiction in West Africa," *Bull. Narc.,* 17:3-13 (Jan., 1965).

35. I. C. Chopra and R. N. Chopra, "The use of the cannabis drug in India," *Bull. on Narc.,* 9(1):23 (Jan.-March, 1957).

36. "The Marijuana Problem in the City of New York," quoted in *The Marijuana Papers,* edited by David Solomon (Indianapolis: Bobbs-Merrill, 1966), p. 283.

37. Haislip, *op. cit.*

38. William F. Quinn, personal communication.

39. Abrams, *op. cit.,* p. 240.

40. "Dependence on cannabis (marijuana)," *J.A.M.A.,* 201:369 (Aug. 7, 1967).

"Oh, Say — Can You See?"

THE LITERATURE OF CANNABIS USE

*"Ye have read, ye have heard, ye
have thought," he said, "and
the tale is yet to run:
By the worth of the body that once
ye had, give answer—what
ha'ye done?"*

—Tomlinson

One of the principal arguments offered by pro-cannabis enthusiasts to "prove" that marijuana has never been indicted as a dangerous drug is that no valid studies have appeared in medical literature which offer sufficient evidence to warrant avoiding the use of cannabis. This is another of the marijuana myths. The reason most people believe it, is that it is continually reiterated, and repetition breeds conviction. The same is true of the refrain, "Pot can't hurt you." In fact, both comments are loaded with error.

If there's nothing in the literature it can be fervently hoped that someone will quickly notify Dr. Oliver Byrd at Stanford University who is currently wading through a United Nations bibliography on marijuana.[1] His review is taking him through more than 1,800 published papers, the overwhelming majority of which condemn cannabis as a dangerous weed. It is, of course, true that there has been a publications gap over the past twenty years as far as new observations on cannabis are concerned. Perhaps this is due to the fact that observers, after publishing so much on the subject, felt it was adequately covered and moved on to study other problems. The new generation, however, particularly in the English-speaking countries, seems intent on reviving the situation again, negating all that has been observed and finding out the hard way facts that have been noted from experience by previous generations in many different cultures and countries.

As a matter of interest, previous studies on this subject have encompassed most of the major languages. To date one can study the following material: 936 articles in English, 386 in French, 206 in German, 106 in Portuguese, 74 in Spanish, 45 in the Slavic languages, 33 in Italian, 12 in Latin, 8 in Dutch, 8 in Turkish, 7 in Russian, 3 in Greek, 3 in Norwegian, 2 in Swedish, and 31 in miscellaneous other languages.

The interesting thing about this material is that so few authors have anything good to say in favor of using cannabis. Those that do, however, are quoted and requoted as though the opinions they express represent the majority view. In truth, the few articles that do express favorable opinions on cannabis are in the smallest minority. Although a few others exist, there are three studies the pro-cannabis people frequently refer to: the Indian Hemp Commission Report published in 1894, a paper that appeared in the *Military Surgeon*[2] dealing with observations begun in the Panama Canal Zone in 1925 and published in 1933, and the so-called La Guardia Report published in 1944.[3]

The report of the Indian Hemp Commission was quite permissive in its findings. It stated that no evidence existed which indicated the use of cannabis caused mental or moral injuries, that it was not associated with disease and that it caused few, if any, effects different from indulgence in alcohol. While one could spend much time dissecting and commenting on the findings in this comprehensive report it should be sufficient for our purposes to note that in 1953 the Indian government decided it had had enough of the effects of cannabis on its culture and authorized a phasing-out program designed to eliminate the use of cannabis in India as quickly as possible.

CANNABIS AND THE MILITARY

There has been a good deal of comment about the use of cannabis by men in the armed forces, especially with the recent disclosures of cannabis use by American troops in Vietnam. Although there have been no recent studies of cannabis use by soldiers, two earlier investigations were undertaken on military personnel in the Panama Canal Zone. These, along with the reports coming from Vietnam, constitute much of the usually quoted knowledge about the use of marijuana by servicemen.

The first study from the Panama Canal Zone was made about 1925 by a committee appointed to investigate the use of marijuana and to recommend corrective procedures to be taken in the event that the committee found the use of the drug was producing detrimental effects on the troops. In essence, after studying the situation for nine months, the committee found that the use of marijuana was not habit forming nor did it have any deleterious influence on the individual using it.

The second Panama Study was carried out in 1931. In this study thirty-four soldiers were hospitalized, given marijuana grown at the Canal Zone Experimental Gardens to assure uniformity of resin content, and their reactions were observed. A controlled environment study of cannabis or any other psychotoxin has certain built-in disadvantages, which will be considered later in treating the La Guardia Report. In any event, the second Panama Study also came up with the observation that cannabis in the Canal Zone is a mild stimulant and intoxicant (apparently Panama Red was not growing there in those days), that it was not habit forming, that crime and antisocial behavior failed to result from its use and that delinquencies caused by marijuana-smoking which might result in the user's being court-martialed were negligible compared to problems caused by the use of alcohol by the troops.

A decade after these studies were printed the editor of the *Military Surgeon* added his observations by expressing the opinion that "the legislation in relation to marijuana was ill-advised, that it branded as a menace and a crime a matter of trivial importance."[4] Perhaps this was true in 1925 and 1931 when few individuals were using it. Perhaps it was of no consequence to a country at peace and able to cope with poor judgment and decreased ability on the part of its soldiers. But what about times when soldiers are facing active combat?

A decade after the Panama articles appeared in the *Military Surgeon* a team of two Army medical officers, Captains Eli Marcovitz and Henry J. Meyers, published their observations made on thirty-five confirmed marijuana addicts who came under their observation during a period of seven months at an army air force regional station hospital. Their findings were published in 1944 in *War Medicine*,[5] a publication of the American Medical Association. Seldom if ever do the pro-cannabis enthusiasts run across these observations.

Pointing out that marijuana "addiction" as a problem both in civil life and in the armed forces has been the subject of controversy and of various viewpoints and conclusions, Marcovitz and Myers objectively expressed their observations on some three dozen men referred to the neuropsychiatric service. Four principal factors brought these men to the attention of the authors: first, chronic physical complaints, usually headache; second, becoming intoxicated on cannabis with uncontrolled behavior patterns or by developing a state approaching stupor; third, disciplinary or delinquency problems, such as demanding from their commanding officers that they be allowed passes to go out and obtain marijuana; and fourth, being arrested because of violence or self-mutilating actions.

The authors stress that their conclusions were based on a specialized group of thirty-five marijuana addicts, namely, a group in military service with difficulties that brought them to the attention of the military or medical authorities. It so happens that in one of the Panama Canal Zone studies a similar group of thirty-four men was observed. The difference is that in Panama the men were in a controlled environment behaving as good drug users are supposed to behave in a controlled study, whereas, those studied by Marcovitz and Myers were seen because of consequences occurring from their behavior in an open, uncontrolled environment. Additionally, the variability of personality factors must be taken into consideration in these as well as is other studies inasmuch as cannabis is an unpredictable drug that produces unpredictable reactions in unpredictable people.

Marcovitz and Myers note that marijuana users

> present a serious problem in their failure to perform any useful duties, in breaches of discipline, in constant need for medical attention, in consistent failure to respond favorably to disciplinary measures or to attempts at rehabilitation and in their disruptive effect on the morale of their organization.
>
> Thirty four [of the users studied] were Negroes, and one was of the white race. As a group, their backgrounds were

heavily loaded with adverse familial, social and economic factors. Their histories were characterized by delinquent and criminal behavior and failure to develop any consistent patterns of productive work. In effect, they felt and acted like enemy aliens toward society.

The personality pictures of such addicts show a typical pattern of response to repeated situations of frustration and deprivation. This consists, on the one hand, of immediate and constant gratification of the need for sensual pleasure and for the feeling of omnipotence, as well as the need to overcome their unbearable anxiety. On the other hand, they show hostility and aggression toward others, especially to authority, with the neurotic repetitive creation of situations which lead to further suffering. The addictive smoking of marijuana serves simultaneously as a satisfaction of all these drives. It is but one aspect of a complex picture of maladjustment.

It is concluded that the problems of disposition of confirmed marijuana addicts of the type described here cannot be solved adequately by punishment, short term imprisonment or discharge from the service. It is recommended that government institutions be created to which such confirmed marijuana addicts may be committed for long term treatment and rehabilitation or for indefinite custody.

The authors' recommendations, of course, were not followed.

Use of cannabis by soldiers in wartime is a different matter from the situations described by previous studies. Late in 1967 a spokesman for the Department of Defense told reporters that the use of marijuana by American troops in Vietnam "is not considered a problem of any consequence."[6] Nevertheless, he added, because of the ready availability of cannabis in Vietnam and the implications of its use by troops, the government was keeping a close watch on the situation. Let's look at the marijuana situation in Vietnam.

The first significant evidence emerged in October, 1967, when John Steinbeck, IV,[7] son of the novelist, was arrested in Washington, D.C., on a narcotics charge. The youth informed the press that three-fourths of his comrades in Vietnam were marijuana smokers. The government denied the charge; nevertheless, between January, 1966, and November, 1967, some

1,500 GI's in Vietnam had been found possessing or using cannabis.[8] Officials recognize this is a low figure since only a segment is apprehended. Additionally the army will not court-martial soldiers on this offense unless the marijuana used as evidence is checked out in laboratory tests. The nearest laboratory to Vietnam is in Japan.

In November, 1967, troop commanders still insisted in their official communiqués that the use of marijuana was not affecting unit efficiency, although they admitted controls were being tightened. At that time, however, Brigadier General Harley Moore, Jr., was quoted as stating that marijuana parties among the troops "have become a problem."[9] About the same time a Department of Defense spokesman, noting arrest figures were representative of a very small percentage of American military strength in Vietnam, said that army statistics indicate that the problem in Vietnam was less serious than among young men in the same age group in the United States. In the same month *Newsweek*[10] magazine asked its correspondent, John Donnelley, for a report on the situation in Saigon. Donnelley replied, "In Da Nang, a serviceman can swap a $2 bottle of PX whiskey for 5 ounces [of cannabis] and bulk purchasing can reduce the cost of 'roll-your-own' reefers to as little as 3 cents each."

Donnelley's report further stated that

> GIs smoke pot everywhere, not just in rear areas. One night in the central highlands, I watched ten GIs light up in a squad tent, while three North Vietnamese divisions lurked only a few miles away just across the Cambodian border. And it is not just soldiers and marines who smoke Mary Jane. It is said that there is not a ship on the Navy's Yankee Station where one cannot get a "joint," and in Saigon there are pot parties in posh villas, where giggling embassy secretaries trade puffs with their junior-official dates.

In December, 1967, despite the reassurance from higher echelons to the general public, military officials ordered an intensified crackdown on marijuana. The decision was precipitated by an army survey that showed one out of every two hundred men was smoking marijuana. "Those arrested," said the Associated Press release,[11] "have included military police, young officers, guards on duty and combat men." Although senior officers could not estimate the actual incidence of use, they did reveal that marijuana-smoking ranked as the single largest major offense among American soldiers in Vietnam.

A bulletin issued by one army division informed its troops that the Viet Cong was supplying marijuana to GI's because they know it makes them ineffective in combat. A 1st Cavalry (Airmobile) Division bulletin amplified just how ineffective the cannabis user could be by warning its men that marijuana decreases effectiveness and makes soldiers subject to "unpredictable and unusual actions such as shooting, grenade throwing, etc." The bulletin went on to state that the enemy was using pushers in an attempt to knock the fighting edge off American troops.[12]

Why are our fighting men turning to cannabis? "You have to realize," an army legal officer told Donnelley, "that in a single division here we have the equivalent of the teen-age and early twenties population of a city of 300,000 in the States." Thinking that one over, Donnelley mused, "What he was saying was that at home these youngsters are the Pot Generation, and despite (or perhaps because of) the dangers of combat, it is unrealistic to expect them to act any differently in Vietnam."[13]

How bad is the situation and how detrimental are the effects of cannabis on American fighting men? No one really knows. Brigadier General Harley Moore, Jr., U.S. Army Provost Marshal, has been quoted as saying he would not be surprised if some GI's were smoking marijuana under combat conditions.[14] Reports to this author from returning GI's tend to corroborate this remark. One youth, a bit dryly observed, "at least they die happy when they go."

The implication of GI's using cannabis in battle is particularly disturbing to authorities. As a Department of Defense spokesman noted in this connection, there can be severe consequences arising from a situation in which "a man who has a gun and may be required to use it—such as a sentry—is high on marijuana."[15]

Another problem is that of returning GI's who have become dependent on cannabis. An unknown quantity of the weed is now entering the United States, much of it undetected, smuggled in by returning "turned-on" servicemen. Additionally, U.S. Customs is having new problems trying to keep out marijuana which GIs are sending home to their families. One might almost wish for the "good old days" back in 1943 when the editor of the *Military Surgeon* in his editorial "The Marijuana Bugaboo" could in clear conscience, based on the Panama Canal Zone studies, refer to cannabis as "a matter of trivial importance."[16]

THE LA GUARDIA REPORT: SOCIOLOGY OF CANNABIS

Turning now to the most frequently quoted study of all, the La Guardia Report, we leave the realm of the hasty, brief, not always well organized study of the effects of cannabis, and find ourselves facing a panel of experts who are truly respected names in medicine. The report came about because at the time of the passage of the Marijuana Tax Act of 1937 the country was caught up in a wave of hysteria concerning the effects of marijuana, particularly as it related to youth.

Fascinating organizations such as the International Narcotic Education Association were publishing diatribes in the guise of "information" that fanned the press and paled the white corpuscles of the readers. "The habitual use of this narcotic poison," one of their publications intoned, ". . . leads to physical wreckage and mental decay. . . . Marijuana sometimes gives man the lust to kill unreasonably and without motive. Many cases of assault, rape, robbery, and murder are traced to the use of marijuana."[17]

On December 28, 1940, the New York *Daily Worker* in its health advice column informed its readers that smoking the weed caused "the face to become bloated, the eyes bloodshot, the limbs weak and trembling and the mind [to sink] into insanity. Robberies, thrill murders, sex crimes and other offenses result." The article went on to say, "the habit can be cured only by the most severe methods. The addict must be put into an institution, where the drug is gradually withdrawn . . . [and] . . . kept there until he has enough willpower to withstand the temptation to again take to the weed."

With all this uproar many public officials had cause for concern. One of these was the mayor of New York City,

F. H. La Guardia. As was his custom in matters of health, he asked for the assistance of the New York Academy of Medicine. The mayor was aware of the paper written concerning the use of marijuana by soldiers stationed in Panama and was impressed by its "relative harmlessness."[18] The mayor wanted factual information that would be a basic contribution to medicine and pharmacology. He also wanted to know how bad the situation was in his city.

The Academy came up with the suggestions of conducting a dual study, one part sociological, one part clinical, to find out (1) the extent of marijuana use in New York City, (2) its method of retail distribution, (3) the attitude of the user toward society, (4) its relationship to sex, (5) its relationship to crime, and (6) its relationship to juvenile delinquency. The sociological study was aimed at finding out the answers to these questions. The clinical study was directed toward the determination, by means of controlled experiments, of the physiological and psychological effects of marijuana on different types of persons, its production or lack of production of mental deterioration, and the potential use of the drug in the treatment of other diseases or addictions.

When pro-cannabis people come together they always eulogize the "Report." In truth, the only thing they usually refer to is the sociological study, being quite careful to leave the impression that this is the sum total of the discoveries of the investigators. They also assiduously avoid mentioning how the sociological section came to its conclusions, all of which are quite favorable toward the use of cannabis. For those who really want to know what happened, this author has a suggestion: read the report. The original is difficult to come by, but a copy is available in Solomon's book *The Marijuana Papers.*[19]

Since the pro-cannabis writers conveniently forget to inform their readers how the sociological conclusions were arrived at, let us take a brief look at the procedures. The reader will probably be just as amazed at what he finds as this author was after he had gone carefully through the whole report. Once again, if in doubt about the findings as presented here, read the La Guardia Report for yourself.

The sociological study begins with a brief review of the

history and notes that there is much dissension concerning the potential of cannabis to produce harm to its users. The authors note briefly the publications of the International Narcotic Education Association and the article in the New York *Daily Worker,* then lump with these zany observations a section of Dr. Robert Walton's book on cannabis that was anything but zany. One of its chapters is "The Present Status of the Marijuana Vice in the United States," written by the Commissioner of Public Safety of New Orleans, Dr. Frank R. Gomila.[20] In this chapter Dr. Gomila refers to his city as being one of the first, if not the first, large city in the United States where the cannabis habit had become firmly established. He noted that reporters had not only heard about but had actually observed large numbers of schoolboys buying and smoking reefers. In one instance a peddler opened shop under the street stairs to a girls' high school.

Inquiries revealed that school children of forty-four schools in New Orleans, only a few being high schools, smoked marijuana. "The Director of Kingsley House for Boys," Gomila noted, "received many pleas from fathers of boys who had come under the influence [of cannabis] and were charged with petty crimes. After personally seeing these boys in an hysterical condition or on the well-known 'laughing jags,' the director termed the situation decidedly grave."[21] As a matter of fact, the situation *was* grave in New Orleans and provided the impetus to legislators to pass the Marijuana Tax Law. This is another fact often "overlooked" by the pro-cannabis people.

The committee of the sociological study of the La Guardia Report, armed with this information, then set about organizing a unit to study the problem in New York. They did not study the entire city of New York. Instead, they chose to study a very limited segment of the city, the borough of Manhattan. All conclusions concerning the rest of New York City were based on what they observed there. The New York Police Department gave the committee four policemen and two policewomen who did the leg work for the observers. The work was strictly undercover, investigative, and infiltrative, with the officers being instructed not to arrest anyone. While on duty the squad lived with and studied marijuana devotees and their habits, although users were presumably unaware of the official capacity of their companions.

The observations made concerning sale, use, and general emotional reactions made by these officers were essentially those previously noted in the literature, i.e., that users were congenial, that they were not "addicted" per se, and that cannabis was transmitted either from user to user or in "teapads" where users congregated. They found one could buy with minimal difficulty after proper introduction and decided from observation that most marijuana was sold either in Harlem or in an area off Broadway between 42nd and 59th Streets.

The undercover agents talked to the users and then relayed the information to the committee which studiously evaluated it. They found most users were unemployed, were aware of the laws, did not use the drug to challenge the laws per se, did not express remorse because they used the drug, and did not blame cannabis for their present personal difficulties. The users all felt the drug was harmless and enjoyed it because it produced a "high," which the committee defined as a feeling of adequacy and efficiency with the allaying of current mental conflicts.

The committee accepted the observations that users were not frustrated if they couldn't find a supply of cannabis, that each user had a limit, past which he would not go because it caused him anxiety, and that the use of cannabis did not lead to the use of hard narcotics. It is well to remember the committee's recognition as it described the sources from which it had arrived at its conclusions that "we have made extensive use of subjective data obtained from those who were actual smokers of marijuana and directly acquainted with its effects and those who were not smokers [i.e., police investigators] but, because of residence, occupation or other interests, were acquainted with the general subject." This last group also, apparently, included many individuals peripherally associated with users, although the committee did not designate who they were.[22]

A point of interest here is that pro-cannabis people so often decry the current papers and in particular papers written in past years in which the observations were based on patients in hospitals and jails because, "the accounts were all subjective." Yet, by the committee's admission, all of their observations in this sociological section were derived from subjective opinions of users as they related, in many instances, their opinions to undercover agents.

The committee then investigated the possible link between sex and cannabis. The investigators acquired their information by visiting many teapads. "It is true," the committee states, "that lewd pictures decorated the walls," but none of the users was interested in them. The pictures just happened to be there. In fact, one police investigator found, to his embarrassment, that he was the only one in the crowd looking at them.

The investigators went to parties and watched jitterbugging, a form of dancing which the committee says "is highly suggestive and appears to be associated with erotic activity." They watched the dancers who were high and those who were not and decided that one group wasn't any more interested in sex than the other. They asked users if they ever associated sex and cannabis and were assured by the users that this rarely occurred. They went to houses of prostitution and were convinced by what they saw (although they didn't say what that was) and noted that, even in those brothels that sometimes doubled as teapads, "the use of marijuana was not linked to sexuality."

On the basis of these findings by police investigators—who must have been the world's most efficient undercover men to be able to mingle with a group well-known for their high index of suspicion, ask personal questions, and peer at their activities—the committee came out with the statement that is considered by many to be the final conclusion on sex and cannabis by the La Guardia Report. "These observations," they said, "allow us to come to the conclusion that in the main marijuana was not used for direct sexual stimulation."[23]

The committee now came to the weighty question of the association of cannabis and crime. Part of their "evidence" consisted of talking to various law enforcement officers and being assured by these police that, speaking off the record and confidentially, "there is no proof that major crimes are associated with the practice of smoking marijuana." Having satisfied themselves that these officers had given them the information they wanted, they then in the next paragraph of their report paid them the following left-handed compliment: "The sale and use of marijuana is a problem engaging the vigilance of the New York Police Department. However, the number of officers available for such duty is limited. Officers specifically assigned to the Narcotics Division of the Police Department are acquainted with the problem, but the *majority of the officers are fundamentally without authoritative knowledge regarding this subject*." (Italics added.) [24]

The committee then read a paper published by respected psychiatrist-in-charge of the Psychiatric Clinic of the Court of General Sessions, Dr. Walter Bromberg, in which he stated that in his experience with respect to marijuana and crime in the Court of General Sessions over a period of five and a half years drugs generally do not initiate criminal careers. Based on the measurement of succession of arrests and convictions in this court, Dr. Bromberg postulated that the expectancy of major crimes following the use of cannabis in New York County would be small. The conclusions of the committee:

1) Marijuana is used extensively in the borough of Manhattan but the problem is not as acute as it is reported to be in other sections of the United States.

2) The introduction of marijuana into this area is recent compared with other localities.

3) The cost of marijuana is low and therefore within the purchasing power of most persons.

4) The distribution and use of marijuana is centered in Harlem.

5) The majority of marijuana smokers are Negroes and Latin Americans.

6) The consensus among marijuana smokers is that the use of the drug creates a definite feeling of adequacy.

7) The practice of smoking marijuana does not lead to addiction in the medical sense of the word.

8) The sale and distribution of marijuana is not under the control of any single organized group.

9) The use of marijuana does not lead to morphine or heroin or cocaine addiction and no effort is made to create a market for these narcotics by stimulating the practice of marijuana smoking.

10) Marijuana is not the determining factor in the commission of major crimes.[25]

The committee now directed its attention to one of the most serious problems—the potential relationship of marijuana to juvenile delinquency. Again they limited their study to the borough of Manhattan. Investigative techniques included: watching schools to see if students bought cannabis from peddlers, investigating parental complaints concerning marijuana usage by their children, interviewing school authorities, and studying statistics from various city bureaus and private agencies.

"Unknown to the school authorities," the committee states, "our investigators had under surveillance many of the schools in the borough of Manhattan. . . . We must admit that it would have been possible for such sales to have taken place during the time that our investigators were not on duty, but we came to the conclusion that there was no organized traffic on the part of peddlers in selling marijuana to the children of the schools we observed."[26]

"Interviews with school authorities," the committee stressed, "were very significant. . . ." And indeed they were, for they exhibit a naïveté of great magnitude exceeded only by the committee's capacity to accept as valid the ability of six policemen to observe adequately marijuana activity at any significant number of schools. As to school authorities, the committee interviewed authorities and/or observed thirty-nine schools. To the committee's delight the principals of thirty-three of these schools said they had no problem. Or almost. Actually what they said was "I have had no trouble. . . ." "I have had no contact with it. . . ." "[I] never found anything to indicate the use of it. . . ." "[I] suspected that a group of chronic truants were using marijuana but [I] was unable to obtain any direct evidence. . . ." "[I know] of no marijuana problem in the school. . . ." "[I] found no tangible evidence. . . ." And so on.

The most fascinating report was that made of School Number 2 which was characteristic of all those schools that under investigation "knew of no marijuana in the school." According to the committee report: "No. 2 High School, Predominantly white. The principal at first appeared to be evasive and did not readily volunteer information, but after repeatedly being pressed with the question stated that the school 'had not had any difficulty with the subject of marijuana.' " One can only sympathize with this poor principal, her job possibly at stake, trying to outmaneuver a group of blue-ribbon officials from the mayor's committee who were trying to find something bad about the students in her school.

In one school where the principal finally admitted there might be a "few" instances of marijuana smoking an assistant to the principal told the committee there had been some boys in the school who had "reefers" in their possession. On other occasions some of the boys appeared to be intoxicated and when examined confessed to having smoked "reefers." The assistant further stated, "It was difficult to be sure if sleepy, perspiring, pallid looking boys were feeling the effects of marijuana or were just recovering from too much 'partying' or 'drinking.' "

A number of principals who "had no contact with it" assured the committee they would notify them immediately if anything turned up. In each instance the committee reports, "During the period of the survey no such report was made."

In another instance where the principal had "no tangible evidence" she did report she believed the drug could be found if one wanted to get it. The committee "investigated thoroughly the suggestions made by the principal as to premises where marijuana might be sold but we were unable to gather any evidence of its sale." In another school the principal reported students claimed that cannabis was on sale in a nearby candy store. Once again the committee "investigated" and came up empty-handed. The pattern was generally repeated in the committee's investigation of schools. In one junior high school where a teacher testified that cannabis had been used and that she had sent home five students she believed to be "dopey" from cannabis, the committee tended to doubt the teacher's word and emphasized that students could be sent home without notification of the principal and without medical examination. The principal had, of course, testified there was no problem in his school.

The committee did not, however, believe everybody. At

School Number 39, for instance, where the principal also reported there was no problem, the committee decided there was indeed a problem. "We are certain, however, that this school does to some extent present an acute problem for we have observed a few students smoking 'reefers' away from the school. We have reason to believe that some of them smoke it while at school. The girls attending this high school have a very low moral standard."

Why the committee took such a dislike to School Number 39 they did not say, but at School Number 32 they were quite willing to accept opinions of the staff. "Although rumor is widespread that 'reefer' smoking is common at this school, thorough investigation did not produce evidence of it at the time of our investigation. We did obtain information," the committee said, "which we consider authoritative, that in 1935 a man was offered the concession to sell marijuana cigarettes to the students of this school. He refused the offer. The principal of this school stated that there had never been any trouble as a result of marijuana smoking and he knew of no actual cases."[27]

On the basis of these observations to which, incidentally, was added a review of the Children's Court records for 1939, the committee came to these conclusions:

1) Marijuana smoking is not widespread among school children.

2) Juvenile delinquency is not associated with the practice of smoking marijuana.

3) The publicity concerning the catastrophic effects of marijuana smoking in New York City is unfounded.[28]

There, briefly, is that part of the La Guardia Report so dear to the hearts of the pro-cannabis people, the part that is quoted and requoted ad infinitum. Further study of the sociological section is left to the reader. Now, let us take a brief look at the part that is not so often quoted but which is significant in that it is to date the only major published clinical observation on a reasonably large number of marijuana smokers.

THE LA GUARDIA REPORT: CLINICAL STUDY

The clinical study was directed toward finding out two

122

main things: the pleasurable effects that account for the wide-spread use of cannabis, and the undesirable effects, "including those leading to criminal and other antisocial acts."[29] There were a number of things about the study which can be criticized in that it was carried on in a locked ward of Goldwater Memorial Hospital, performed under the direct observation of guards from the Department of Corrections and the New York City Police Force, and participated in by seventy-two prisoners from either Rikers or Hart Island penitentiaries or the House of Detention for Women plus five paid volunteers who had had no previous experience with cannabis. Only one of these was considered to be a normal personality.[30]

This general picture is a bit gloomy, but the investigators had to start somewhere and they should be given credit for trying. The subjects numbered sixty-five males and seven females, with forty-eight having a history of smoking marijuana previously. The committee notes that there were two advantages in selecting subjects from this group. First, they could be kept under continuous observation and second, they constituted an excellent sample of the "typical" New York City user.

There were also some disadvantages. Being under constant observation and in custody the subjects were in no position to try anything original. This meant they did not dare permit themselves to become so high on cannabis they could not control their activities. Secondly, at least forty-eight of the group were "street smart"; they knew that the best way to get along in jail is to cooperate and give the "man" what he wants. The group had an average IQ of nearly one hundred and they knew from experience that they could not get out of line without retribution. Even so, the clinical study reveals a number of important findings that are seldom referred to by the pro-cannabis people. These findings, chosen here at random from the report, can be read in their original context by those who wish to increase their knowledge on the techniques employed by the physicians who worked with this study.[31]

1) Various states of marijuana intoxication were precipitated by varying doses of the drug. These ranged from the usual euphoria and incoordination with smaller amounts, to

feelings of discomfort and depression, and with one subject a state of depression with anxiety after taking the equivalent of four joints and a psychotic episode with a fear of death when he doubled this amount.

2) The subjects varied considerably in their general behavior after taking the drug. Quite commonly, they demonstrated a difficulty in focusing and in sustaining mental concentration.

3) The investigators did note that eroticism was reported in 10 percent of the 150 instances in which marijuana was administered to the group. "The presence of nurses, attendants and other women associated with the study gave opportunity for frank expression of sexual stimulation, had this been marked."[32] The observers did not include in this observation the fact that the presence of guards also gave the subjects the opportunity for a slap in the head if they got too far out of line. On the other hand, some subjects did lose control and in isolated instances would loudly discharge flatus or urinate on the floor, while one man who had been previously arrested on three occasions for indecent exposure indulged in frank exhibitionism.

4) The general behavior of the group was interesting. They argued but "the arguments never seemed to get anywhere, although they often dealt with important problems, and the illogical reasoning used was never recognized or returned by the person to whom it was addressed." The committee also noted, "it is obvious that under marijuana the subject laughs more readily and for longer time intervals. This is probably due both [to] the fact that things seem funnier to him and because when under the influence of the drug he is less inhibited." Further, the committee noted, "One forgot that these were actually adults with all the usual adult responsibilities. One could not help drawing the conclusion that they too had forgotten this for the time being."[33] But the committee report insisted that, "although urged to smoke more, no subject could be persuaded to take more than he knew or felt he could handle."

5) The problem of psychotic episodes has been mentioned before but is repeated briefly again because of its importance:

"The conclusion seems warranted that given the potential personality make-up and the right time and environment, marijuana may bring on a true psychotic state."[34]

6) The more complex the activity engaged in under the influence, the more the activity is affected. Simple functions such as tapping are affected only slightly, whereas complex functions such as hand-steadiness and complex reaction time "may be affected adversely to a considerable degree by the administration of both large and small doses of marijuana."[35]

7) Marijuana has a transitory adverse effect on mental functioning. The extent of the intellectual impairment, the time of onset, and its duration are all related to the amount of drug taken. In general, the nonusers experienced greater intellectual impairment for longer periods of time than that experienced by those who had used cannabis before. Because speed and accuracy are affected, the user finds he has a falling off of ability. Indulgence in marijuana, however, does not appear to result in mental deterioration.[36]

8) Individuals under the influence of marijuana do not change their basic personality structure. They do, however, experience increased feelings of relaxation, disinhibition, and self-confidence, the latter tending to be expressed verbally more than physically. The disinhibition releases what is latent in the individual's thoughts and emotions but does not evoke responses that would be alien to him in the undrugged state. The use of marijuana not only releases pleasant reactions but also feelings of anxiety. Where personality is concerned, the people most likely to resort to the use of marijuana are those who have difficulty making satisfactory social contacts or experiencing emotional reactions.[37]

9) These subjects who were tested for attitude changes showed very little change of opinion toward family and community when they were under the influence of marijuana. The only very definite change was in their attitude toward the drug itself. Without marijuana only four out of fourteen subjects tested said they would tolerate the sale of marijuana. After they were up on the drug eight of them were in favor of this. Another significant reaction observed was that subjects who were up on marijuana were content to live in a community

that was less orderly and well organized than when they were not influenced by the drug. This, the observers felt, might be due to the generally indifferent attitude and the lack of motor coordination caused by the effects of the drug.[38]

This, briefly, is a summary of the findings of the clinical study section of the La Guardia Report. It should be unnecessary at this stage of discussion of marijuana to point out the relevance of these findings to the social aspects of the use of cannabis by those individuals who are marginally adjusted prior to coming under the influence of the drug. Realization that it is this sort of person that is attracted to the continued use of the drug makes the observations of this study even more socially significant.

It is unfortunate that the La Guardia Report has been discounted by so many who apparently failed to read the significant findings of the clinical study. It is equally sad that the sociological findings are so often stressed when a survey of the techniques used to arrive at the final conclusions fails to stand critical scrutiny. This, however, has been the story of marijuana: confused, distorted, multifaceted, misunderstood, feared, exalted, misinterpreted. Perhaps, someday, a final study will be done to clear away all doubt in the minds of both proponents and opponents. As it stands at the moment, however, only a few writers of scientific standing have come out in favor of the use of the drug, and the literature in general is overwhelmingly critical, even condemnatory, of the use of the drug. Fortunately for man, all this discussion is limited to a unique plant with but a single genus and species. If there were more than one it is difficult to see how the world could survive the controversy.

1. Oliver Byrd, personal communication.

2. *Indian Hemp Drugs Commission Report,* (Government Printing Office: 1893-94) 7 vol.; "Marijuana Smoking in Panama," *Milit. Surg.,* 73:269-280 (1933).

3. New York City Mayor's Committee on Marijuana, *The Marijuana Problem in the City of New York* (Lancaster, Pa.: Jacques Cattell Press, 1944.

4. James M. Phalen, "The Marijuana Bugaboo," *Milit. Surg.,* 93:94-95 (1943).

It seems to be logical that a man has a right to do damn near anything he chooses until he interferes with the rights of others to do damn near anything they choose to do. The exceptions to this must of course be where violence or coercion are [sic] involved.

If doing your thing involves vegetating or becoming so dependent on any stimulant (booze, drugs, religion) that you are unable to function as a human being then it appears that someone, somehow, should have a right to restrain you. We would not like to have the job. We would not like to say when you have gone too far.

Doing your thing should be considered as a contribution to the welfare of yourself and your fellowman. If it does not do either of these it would appear to be a bummer.

      —Editorial, *Haight Ashbury Freepress*, 1:2, 1968

Though it may come as a surprise to many, hippies do believe in law. The problem arises in that many hippies choose to determine for themselves which laws are proper and which are of such little value that they should be ignored. In the latter class most hippies fervently place the marijuana laws, feeling they are constitutionally invalid because they deprive people of the right to "do their own thing" in ways that "don't hurt anybody." Unfortunately for those who run into conflict with cannabis laws, this flexibility of thinking is not permitted by legislation. And while some may agree with Dickens' Mr. Bumble that at times "the law is an ass," it is the law nevertheless and those who run afoul of it often suffer severe consequences. That is what all the discussion is about where the law and cannabis is concerned.

Back in the days when, to adopt Lindesmith's point of view, only "bad" people were caught and prosecuted under the marijuana tax laws, no one seemed to care very much. Now that the scene has changed and "good kids" are involved in using marijuana, people *are* beginning to care. But too many are unconcerned about encouraging youngsters to obey the laws. Instead they are directing their energies toward changing the marijuana laws just as America did in past years with the Volstead Act on the principle that, since people are using the stuff, we might as well make it legal so the kids won't find themselves in peril.

Writers such as Rosevear never tire of telling us that the laws are at fault, not the people who choose to use the drug in defiance of the laws. The laws, states Rosevear,[1] cause the user to become paranoid. "It appears," he says, "that the anti-marijuana laws are solely responsible for his [the user's] paranoia, and not that the drug per se causes any such emotion." Of course, the user has no driving need to take cannabis; it is instead a matter of his resenting the prohibition of his enjoyment. "He does not need the drug, it must be understood," Rosevear[2] advises us, "but the pleasant prospect of having it when he wants it overcomes his fear of being caught." The reason one smokes the weed in the face of severe legal opposition, says Rosevear,[3] is that "the occasional smoker feels that if he quits smoking because of fear, he is somehow a liar, and a puppet of an unjust law."

Further, Rosevear[4] tells us that the users are "dangerous in that they are not obeying the doctrines of law that have been so carefully written to protect them. Their activity is deviant. Because of the law, their meetings must be kept secret. And because they experience a sensation that is relatively forbidden, they frequently act a little smug." Smug or not, however, Rosevear assures us, the pot smoker really doesn't like to be an outcast from the rest of society. In fact he "has a great deal of difficulty in adjusting to the position of being on the 'other side' of the law. As his resentment grows," says Rosevear,[5] "he develops the attitude that the police aren't really serving in the capacity as 'defenders of rights,' but that they are infringing on the smoker's rights to smoke. This change in attitude may, admittedly, be a cause for a criminal attitude, and then, after the feeling is developed, even a justification for a crime. After all, the smoker may think, what could be less criminal-like than quietly sitting in a room?"

Rosevear likes to think there has been no change in the user picture since 1937 when the anti-marijuana laws were first passed. In fact, he says, the only thing that has changed in the drug picture since 1937 is the passage of these laws. "Perhaps, because of the Federal Marijuana Tax Act, marijuana users suddenly had no choice but to deal with those who knew the drug picture," he comments in a sort of off-the-cuff explanation as to why cannabis users tend to consort with some underworld elements. "In other words," he reasons, "it is possible that the association of marijuana and heroin was brought about because of the antimarijuana law."[6]

Perhaps it's good to have something to blame for the current increase in cannabis use. Certainly no one person likes to think he is responsible, so, if nothing else, it's convenient to blame the laws. One could say the same for the man who violates the speed limit on an empty highway and is arrested: he was hurting no one, and the law has made him a criminal. . . .

THE LAW AND ITS ENFORCEMENT

If indeed the law is at fault, it all began some thirty years ago, in 1937, when the Marijuana Tax Act was passed by Congress. It was passed because legislators were convinced that the use of cannabis was getting out of control in America just as it had so many times in the past in other nations where it had acquired at least a quasi-social acceptance. Inflamed by lurid stories in the press and appalled by testimony by men

131

such as New Orleans District Attorney Eugene Stanley that many of the crimes of the South were committed by criminals who relied on the effects of the drug to give them a false courage and freedom from restraint, the law was passed in an attempt to prevent further contamination, particularly of American youth, by the habit of smoking cannabis.

The Marijuana Tax Act, patterned after the Harrison Narcotic Act, attempted to curb the use of cannabis by employing federal police power and by the imposition of penalties upon both buyers and sellers. These penalties were increased in 1951 and again in 1956 by the passage of the Federal Narcotics Control Act. In essence, the marijuana law provides that sales of cannabis must be accompanied by the payment of a transfer tax of $1.00 per ounce in legitimate sales and $100.00 per ounce if sold to unapproved purchasers, the latter transfer being considered illegal and prohibited. Punishment on the federal level for violation of the Act may result in maximum sentences of from ten to forty years, depending on the offense, if one possesses, sells, or gives away cannabis without filling in the prescribed federal form. The tax obviously is designed to make it extremely difficult to acquire cannabis for abusive use and to develop an adequate means of publicizing dealings in the drug in order to tax and control the traffic effectively.

In addition to federal control, each state has its own laws that regulate and monitor traffic in all dangerous drugs, including cannabis. The specificity of the law and the penalties provided vary from state to state, but in general the state laws are patterned after the Uniform Narcotic Drug Act which is similar to federal law in its controls. Interestingly, federal law, which places controls over cannabis in a manner similar to that imposed on narcotics by the Harrison Narcotic Act of 1914, does not consider cannabis to be a narcotic. State laws, however, tend to define it as such, a point of definition which has been declared fully legal by the Supreme Court of Colorado.[7]

Despite the presence on the books of federal and state laws, marijuana violations are on an alarming upswing. In many cases misinformation from adults has led young people to believe the penalties are less severe than they are, and of course publicity through communications media has contributed an air of glamor to the use of cannabis. The result has been, in the words of *Life*[8] magazine, "the greatest mass flouting of the law since Prohibition."

Just what conviction for violating marijuana laws can mean was made clear by Judge John H. Saunders[9] of the Santa Anita, California, Municipal Court in a recent address: "I am heartsick," he told a young audience, "over the number of young people who come into my court charged with narcotics violations. Many of them, I felt, really didn't know the consequences." These consequences," the Judge informed his audience, "can be severe and the time spent in prison is the least of it. When the convict is released from prison, he becomes a second-class citizen economically. . . . Persons convicted of a felony in narcotics cases will not be licensed by the state in a wide variety of fields ranging from accounting and medicine to engineering and funeral directing.

"You can't even be a barber," he warned, "and most school districts will not hire teachers with a conviction on their records and the government will not give them clearance to work in the defense industry."

"No amount of discussion about the appropriateness of the state narcotics law," warns Yale University Dean Georges May,[10] "can detract from the hard fact that at the present time possession, use or distribution of illegal drugs, including marijuana, makes anyone involved with narcotics, even in a single experiment carried out in the privacy of one's room, liable to arrest, conviction, fine and imprisonment.

"Regardless of the ultimate disposition of the case in courts," he continued, "the arrested student is immediately faced with the heavy financial burdens of bail money and legal fees, which often exceed $1,000. The long range expense to the student may be even greater. Moreover, a conviction for a narcotics law violation may preclude consideration for graduate or professional school acceptance, disqualify for graduate fellowships, jeopardize employment opportunities upon graduation and be a source of personal disadvantage for the convicted student for the rest of his life."

The Federal Bureau of Narcotics quite properly notes that in its jurisdiction students and the occasional user have not been prosecuted. But this is not true in states where young people have been arrested under state law. There, the rigidity of the laws has sometimes resulted in the imposition of penalties that were out of proportion to the seriousness of the crime. This has resulted in senseless prison time being imposed on casual users or juvenile offenders, a punishment that has been both cruel and ineffective. In some instances misguided jurists have sent users to jail to "cure" a nonexistent "addiction." Jails being what they are, these individuals, registered as criminals with all this label implies, have been forced in some instances into a criminal existence by those very forces sworn to prevent crime.

On the other side of the coin, juries have failed to convict drug abusers who were actually involved in criminal activity but whose concomitant use of marijuana has involved such unreal sentences that the process of justice seemed distorted. Still, we must have laws to protect society from those who cannot control themselves, for in the area of cannabis abuse there seem to be many who are ready, willing, and able to become cannabis converts.

"It is well to realize," as Royal Canadian Mounted Police Commissioner George B. McClellan[11] has noted, "that for every freedom, right or privilege we enjoy in a democratic society there must be an equal and compensating sense of responsibility and an absolute requirement for self-discipline. When one exercises freedom without responsibility, without self-discipline, he is like an engine without a governor and runs wild. The system of law which we have today exists, or should exist, to maintain that balance between rights and responsibilities."

There is yet one further dimension to existing anti-marijuana laws, one that is almost entirely neglected by those who advocate the repeal of present restrictions on the possession and use of cannabis: the participation of the United States in an international agreement, The Single Conventions Treaty of 1961, signed by the President and ratified by the U.S. Senate on May 8, 1967. This treaty requires that the United States, along with some seventy-three nations of the World Health Organization, include cannabis among the dangerous drugs that should be prohibited. This treaty, as determined in a decision rendered by the U.S. Supreme Court in the case of *Missouri vs. Holland*,[12] is considered along with similar treaties to be the law of the land along with the United States Constitution.

The treaty[13] sets as its goal the elimination of the use of cannabis in member countries over the next twenty-five years. It hopes to do this by education and by legal means in countries where it has previously been legal to use the drug. The World Health Organization also strongly recommended that no country where marijuana is now illegal should change its status. To have entered into this treaty only to renege on its enforcement would place the United States in a most undesirable position and it seems improbable this will occur.

Such then is the broad picture of the law as it stands. But perhaps the most striking thing about anti-marijuana laws today is that they are under continued attack. An adequate picture of the present legal situation requires some consideration also of the fight to legalize cannabis.

SOME RECENT LEGAL SKIRMISHES

For two decades or so the anti-marijuana laws created little stir in the nation, but in the last half-dozen years they have come under severe attack. No doubt many deep underlying causes have contributed to the change but on the more identifiable level one can note simply a change in fashion. It is, quite simply, "in" to be "for pot" and "square" to be against it. Given ten speakers at a symposium, nine against the use of the drug and one for it, and the headlines will feature the remarks of the pro-cannabis speaker. Where twenty-five years ago the communications media spread horror stories about the danger of cannabis, these same media, and some new ones, now seem to be contributing to its popularity.

Some remarkable people have also joined the pro-cannabis forces. In Los Angeles in late 1967 the presiding judge of the juvenile department of the Los Angeles Superior Court made headlines by stating he felt the use of marijuana should "be left to the good judgement of every adult."[14] The judge's statements were not wholly consistent throughout, for he admitted that, like alcohol, cannabis should be restricted for use by minors and that even for adults marijuana might become as serious a problem as alcohol. Still, he expressed an opinion in favor of individual adult choice in the matter of using marijuana.

For his efforts the Judge found himself transferred out of juvenile court by his presiding judge.[15] "I am afraid," his superior said, "that his statements concerning the controversial drug have destroyed his value in the juvenile department." Concern about remarks of this type has been voiced by many authorities in the field of drug abuse. "If we legalize marijuana [of the American type]," Dr. Donald Louria warns, "are we not taking the first steps to legitimize the widespread use of more potent hallucinogens with all their immense potential dangers? With legalization, inevitably there would develop in this country a substantial number of chronic, excessive users, thus encouraging the likelihood of chronic psychosis and criminality."[16]

Indeed, one of the concerns most frequently expressed by those who oppose legalization is the possible creation of a large body of drug-dependent persons who would become drains on society. Attorney Gene Haislip, advisor to the former Federal Bureau of Narcotics, says that we cannot know what kind of problems might result from legalization. "It would take a generation of permissiveness to discover how many millions would eventually become dependent, turn to narcotic addiction, fill the asylums, jails and hospitals. If we permit the legalization of marijuana on the basis of our inability to unequivocally prove how much worse legalized marijuana would be than legalized alcohol, then by the same standard we cannot continue to prohibit the abuse of narcotics, amphetamines, barbiturates, LSD, or any other drug. This would seem to be the absurd conclusion of an absurd logic."[17] Such authorities as Dr. Sidney Cohen and Yale psychologist Kenneth Keniston agree with this point and warn that the consequences to both the individual and the society as a whole are at this point incalculable.

While the authorities debate, the problem confronts more and more people. "When only the poor sought paradise by way of pot," says Ferdinand Mount,[18] "nobody cared about the enhancement and enrichment of perception. They just flung 'em in jail." Observing that today as their own children are being caught in the web of enforcement a new breed of marijuana supporter is arising from the middle class and/or intellectual drug-taker group, Mount says,

> I note also a new snobbery emerging, namely that it is a mistake to enforce the laws against marijuana because this cultivates a disrespect for the law among students who are well able to distinguish between the dangers of pot and heroin.
>
> The opening of the drug world in all its glowing illusion to the children of the middle class has revealed absolutely no superiority of moral intelligence. The distinction (as usual in matters of self-destructive indulgence) is not between income or IQ groups but between the morally and spiritually strong and the morally and spiritually weak. There is little evidence that the children of the college professor are necessarily better able to deal sensibly with drugs than the children of the poor. The only difference is that until recently the professor's children had little or no contact with drugs.

For the most part enforcement personnel have stood foursquare against the watering down of present narcotics laws as they pertain to cannabis. At a recent meeting of the California Narcotic Law Enforcement Officers Association in 1967 the convention adopted a resolution that said:

> Recognizing that inadequate control of the illicit marijuana traffic breeds drug dependence, creates enforcement problems and injures the national welfare: therefore, be it resolved that the federal and state laws controlling marijuana be retained in a form which will insure that illicit traffickers will be severely dealt with, and that the possession of marijuana be restricted under criminal penalty to legitimate medical, scientific, research and industrial use.

In agreement, Los Angeles Police Chief Thomas Reddin[19] says: "Until the truth of the problem is known law enforcement must cope with the current abuse problem." He is perfectly willing, the chief says, to "let the scientists and lawmakers take over, and when they find the total answer, we will do as they say. Until then, policemen must enforce the law as it's written now. Based on the findings of men I've spent most of my adult career working with," he says, "men who have worked with the marijuana problem, I have to conclude the drug should be outlawed. In the absence of scientific proof otherwise, I couldn't change my mind."

The issue turns again and again to learning the full truth about the effects of cannabis. The problem is that controlled trials, the few that have been made (including the clinical study of the La Guardia Report) have all tended to disrupt the dreams of cannabis smokers by declaring that, at best, cannabis has nothing to offer its users but an unreal illusionary state or temporary euphoria and, at worst, significant emotional and mental harm. Pro-cannabis forces continue to push for more studies, presumably in the hope that a favorable one will emerge. Even more strongly they push for legalization, even without the studies. One such force,[20] suggested that "a group of dedicated attorneys should prepare a 'marijuana test case' worthy of consideration before the highest court in the land." They may yet obtain their wish, but it may not win them their goal. So far the closest thing to a major test case has been the Boston trial of 1967.

THE BOSTON MARIJUANA CASE

The Boston case was fought by Joseph Oteri, a cheerful, disarming, pipesmoking defense attorney who also, interestingly, serves as a counsel for the National Association of Police Officers.[21] The marijuana law "gripes me," he recently said, "the hazards of marijuana are a myth." But Oteri appears to be intent, not on legalizing the drug or promoting its use, but instead, on eliminating the current laws which he feels are poor and starting over with proper drug legislation. So motivated, he undertook the defense of a marijuana violation in Boston.

The facts in the case were that Oteri's two clients were arrested at Logan International Airport in East Boston on March 11, 1967, when one of the defendants presented a claims check for a trunk at the baggage counter which contained fifty pounds of sand and five pounds of marijuana. They were tried and convicted of violations of the state's marijuana laws on two counts and sentenced to jail. The defendants appealed the decision on the grounds that the laws relating to the possession, use, and sale of marijuana in the Commonwealth of Massachusetts were unconstitutional because they were arbitrary, irrational, and unsuited to the accomplishment of any valid legislative purpose. They also argued that their rights had been violated under the Ninth Amendment to the U.S. Constitution and by the Due Process and Equal Protection Clauses of the Fourteenth Amendment. They claimed that the statutes imposed cruel and unusual punishment on users, possessors, and sellers of marijuana in violation of the Eighth Amendment as applied to the states by the Fourteenth Amendment.

The defendants pled their case before the Chief Justice of the Superior Court, G. Joseph Tauro. Judge Tauro deliberated on the findings through a mountain of testimony equally divided between those who felt cannabis posed a social and individual threat, and those who felt it was basically an innocuous weed. After three months he returned the judgment that, "It is my opinion, based on the evidence presented at this hearing, that marijuana is a harmful and dangerous drug." The judge went on to give a thorough summary[22] of the effects of marijuana and finally concluded with a lengthy statement on the arguments about the use and sociology of marijuana and the desirability of its legalization, much of which is repeated here because it constitutes the most recent high-level legal judgment on cannabis in the United States:

> To my knowledge, this has been the most extensive, judicial inquiry into the legal and factual aspects concerning the use of marijuana. At this hearing, many eminently well qualified experts on the subject from here and abroad have had their opinions subjected to searching cross-examination and careful analysis by learned and thoroughly prepared counsel. One of the principal factual issues presented for determination is whether marijuana is a harmful and dangerous drug. Several legal issues are raised by defendants' motion to dismiss, but basically this is the question which requires an answer.
>
> I found the testimony of the experts in the various branches of science very illuminating and helpful—although often controversial. On the other hand, there were areas of agreement among them, which are delineated elsewhere in this decision.
>
> Of grave and immediately apparent importance is the

growing appeal marijuana has for young people of high school and college age and for those having underlying instabilities or personality disorders of varying degrees. In many instances, the ones least capable of coping with the mind altering effects of the drug are the ones most likely to be adversely affected by its use.

The serious effects of marijuana superimposed upon mental and personality disorders have been described at length and in great detail by competent experts. I find this testimony persuasive. Actually, there is little, if any dispute, in this area between the defendants' experts and the Commonwealth's experts. Furthermore, all of them testified that they do not advocate the use of marijuana.

In its application to youngsters of high school and college age, the problems presented by the use of this drug assume tremendous proportions. There is no persuasive evidence that its use produces any beneficial results. The defense asserts that the drug causes no direct physical harm. Neither do heroin and other "hard" drugs, but few youngsters dare to experiment with these. Unfortunately, many marijuana users do not have the same apprehension or fear concerning its use, as they do of the physically addictive drugs. This, I feel, is one of the real dangers which permeates the problem. Marijuana is likely to be used, at least initially, as a lark, as an adventure without fear of serious consequences. Thus, the first and apparently innocuous step may be taken in a succession of others possibly leading to drastic results.

This phase of the problem is further complicated by those who unwittingly and perhaps unintentionally create the impression that marijuana is harmless, because it is not physically addictive. The young seize upon such utterances to rationalize their conduct.

While it is generally agreed that marijuana does not cause *physical* addiction as do heroin and the other "hard" narcotics, there was ample and compelling testimony that its use causes psychological dependence. Its users may not be driven to its repeated use by a physical craving, but they may come to resort to it habitually in order to compensate for real or imagined inadequacies or to avoid real or imagined problems. This pernicious and insidious form of addiction is sometimes the first step in the direction of the more potent or physically addictive drugs.

It is a universally accepted fact that marijuana is a mind altering drug and is used for that specific purpose. It is also a generally accepted fact that the drug has no medically recognized therapeutic value. In addition to its adverse effect on ill-adjusted persons, at best, it provides an insubstantial crutch to its user, giving him a feeling of intoxication in varying degrees. It provides a false sense of capabilities, strength and courage. This is of great importance when the drug user is faced with a problem which demands exercise of judgment and where the drug substitutes a euphoric and unreal feeling of exhilaration for the calm and logical thinking required by the circumstances.

In place of positive thinking and positive action, the user's mind is altered and distorted causing serious interference with his powers of perception and coordination and his ability to judge the passage of time and space.

The defendants assert that marijuana provides a certain amount of happiness or relaxation without harmful results. I am not persuaded by the evidence that the resulting euphoria is, in fact, a pleasurable and rewarding experience. I remain unconvinced by the evidence that the average user is made happy or contented—even for a short period of time. The normal brain function is altered or suspended, making the user more susceptible to the influence of others. The use of the drug also tends to accentuate any tendency toward improper conduct. In addition, it induces an abnormally subjective concentration on trivia. In short, marijuana produces a state which is analogous to a temporary mental aberration. Its prolonged and excessive use may induce a psychotic state, especially in those individuals with pre-existing psychological problems.

In my opinion a proper inference may be drawn from the evidence that there is a relationship between the use of marijuana and the incidence of crime and anti-social behavior. Within the limitations of our present statistical information, we can only speculate as to the precise nature and scope of the relationship. This is, to a certain degree, the hidden aspect of the problem. We cannot, at present, ascertain to what extent marijuana is a contributing factor in motor vehicle and other accidents, school dropouts, criminal activity, cases of "hard" narcotics addiction, broken homes and ruined careers, irrational and deviate acts, or losses of ambition and of the desire to become productive members of society. Although the *extent* of such results may be speculative, it is my opinion that a strong inference may be drawn from the evidence presented at this hearing that a causal relationship does exist between the use of marijuana and those assorted social evils. In order to establish more firmly the nature and scope of this relationship, exhaustive and incisive studies must be undertaken.

In any event, there is no indication from the evidence that the user of marijuana becomes, through its use, a better student, a better worker, more dedicated to the public interest, or more efficient or productive in any undertaking. On the contrary, there is convincing evidence that the converse is true.

Many succumb to the drug as a handy means of withdrawing from the inevitable stresses and legitimate demands of society. The evasion of problems and escape from reality seem to be among the desired effects of the use of marijuana. Its use is not so much a symbol of dissent in order to effectuate changes in our social system, but rather a manifestation of a selfish withdrawal from society.

The lessons of history and the experiences of other nations teach us that such artificial alteration of the normal brain function by the use of drugs has been harmful both to the individual and to society in which he lives. The evidence clearly indicates that where a sub-culture has developed which tolerates the general use of marijuana or its derivatives, the harmful results have become clearly manifest. It is of great significance that the vast majority of nations have outlawed its use.

Although its relevancy is doubtful, there was the unavoidable comparison of marijuana with alcohol. Alcohol has some therapeutic value and its use is not limited solely to the achievement of a state of intoxication or the alteration of the mental processes. Furthermore, the use of alcohol is supported here and elsewhere by many centuries of cultural experience. Admittedly, its misuse has posed serious problems and continues to do so. But these problems, as they now exist, could be greatly expanded and compounded by the legalization of the use of marijuana. It is difficult to justify any law which would permit an expansion in the use of marijuana to the point where conceivably it would fall into the same category as alcohol and become a part of our national culture. That the use of marijuana may have results similar to those associated with the abuse of alcohol is hardly a persuasive argument for its legalization.

Marijuana users must, of necessity, consort with opportunistic pushers and other hardened members of the criminal element. In the case of youngsters, this is especially dangerous. It introduces them to and establishes a rapport with persons whose total influence is apt to be corruptive. As serious, if not more so, as the young user's association with pushers and the criminal element is the frequency, duration and intimacy of his contacts with other basically unstable users who not only involve him in their problems but compound his own.

The defendants argue that the statutes are also criminogenic in nature, as well as cruel and unusual, in that they prescribe serious criminal penalties for what may be relatively minor offenses. These arguments certainly do not apply to pushers. The legislation might profitably be reviewed with regard to the penalties provided for possessors as opposed to pushers or where the evidence indicates a first offense with the improbability of repetition. In such cases, the judge should be given wide discretionary powers so that the imposition of a criminal record may be avoided whenever warranted by the facts.

TRENDS IN THE LAW

Judge Tauro's final paragraph reminds us that more and more legislators are asking whether we ought to review and possibly rewrite state laws pertaining to the control of cannabis. More often than not the answer arrived at is, yes. The argument most often advanced from the legislative point of view for modifying cannabis laws is that existing laws have not been effective; violations have been on the increase and they have bred disrespect for law and order. On the other side many counter with the argument that total effectiveness is not the ultimate test of whether a law is good or not and that, in any case, much effective work has been done by existing laws, such as the prevention in the main of availability of the higher-potency hashish type of cannabis from the United States and the deterrence of persons who might have entered into the sale of marijuana for profit.

Ferdinand Mount[23] argues,

The fact that people evade a law does not mean that the law in question is unworkable, still less that it is undesirable. Many traffic violations go unpunished; many of the punishments go unpaid. There are hundreds of thousands of scofflaws in New York State alone. This does not indicate that the majority of people oppose the laws, nor that the police do not attempt to enforce them, but merely that universal enforcement would be a task far exceeding the capacity of the police. The laws and their partial enforcement do have an effect on the behavior of motorists, nevertheless. Similarly with marijuana. It is not now sold in stores. Though access is now far from difficult, many young people who might fear not to try marijuana as a badge of manhood were its use legal, do not bother to under present restrictions—or not more than once or twice. Forbidden fruit may be sweeter but most of us are too lazy to climb over the wall after it.

In regard to whether restrictive laws work or not, it is intresting to note that Great Britain, which has recently instituted an anti-alcohol, safe-driving program utilizing a breathalyzer law, has managed to acquire a marked drop in traffic accidents. That there is a direct correlation is suggested by the statistics that reveal nighttime pub sales have dropped off as much as 25 percent during the same period that nighttime road accidents declined 42 percent. No doubt there continue to be those in England who drink and have accidents. According to pro-cannabis logic the British law ought therefore to be repealed.

Meantime, legislators throughout the nation continue to wrestle with the problem of whether to modify, repeal, or let stand existing marijuana laws. "Except for narcotics agents, police officers, and bewildered and heartsick parents who have discovered their children to be drug users," says California Assemblyman Pete Wilson,[24]

California lawmakers suffer perhaps the most acute frustration of all those attempting to deal with the problem. The success of attempted legislative curbs on drug use is not accurately measurable. No one can say for certain what the juvenile drug arrest figures would be in the absence of present legislation but the hard fact is: it has not prevented the sharp rise in arrests that so alarms us.

We are compelled [Wilson admits] "to re-examine the laws we have enacted, and to consider new approaches. Our efforts to date have been chiefly in the area of defining and proscribing the use of intoxicating substances thought to be harmful; on occasion of increasing penalties for violation; of attempting to remove juvenile users from schools so as to avoid "contamination" of non-user students; and finally of requiring instruction in our public schools in the hazards of drug use. Legislating against drug use is fraught with problems.

In October, 1967, California State Senator Anthony Beilenson held a meeting of the California Senate Public Health and Safety Committee for the purpose of acquiring up-to-date information and opinion in the field of marijuana because he felt it likely that various bills would be introduced into the state legislature in the forthcoming months which would attempt to effect changes in the state's marijuana laws. As usual, a considerable amount of conflicting testimony was introduced and, as usual, it reflected concern on the part of individuals of varying experience with marijuana as a drug of abuse as relates to the current crop of high school and college youngsters who have chosen to violate existing laws in order to try or to continue to use the drug.

A series of pertinent observations was offered by Los Angeles County Deputy District Attorney Joe Reichman,[25] whose job it is to file all marijuana complaints in his area. Expressing his own opinions and not those of his office, Mr. Reichman said: "I thought if I were a legislator, and I had the task of attempting to revise the marijuana laws, I would want to know the answers to some of the questions. I would want to know what the cost of enforcing the marijuana laws is, and how effective that enforcement is. I would want to know whether there is any relationship between the use of marijuana and the commission of subsequent crimes, and I would also want to know what effect the use of marijuana had upon the user."

Reciting current statistics concerning marijuana arrests (at the time of testimony they constituted 17½ percent of all felonies issued by the Los Angeles District Attorney's downtown office, excluding those arrests where no complaint was made), Reichman expressed the opinion that the cost of enforcing the laws was very high and suggested that consideration be given as to whether or not it is worth the cost to continue enforcing these laws. Reichman testified:

Every time an arrest takes place, it usually involves two police officers, and several hours are involved. There is the initial interrogation, the arrest, the transportation of the defendant to the police station, the booking, the preparation of the police report; two or three hours go by without any difficulty at all. A police officer on an eight-hour shift could normally not handle more than two or three arrests during this particular period. Add to it the cost of the police officer coming to court. They have to appear twice. They have to appear at a preliminary hearing. This involves easily a half day in our crowded courts.

Then, there is the matter of the trial. That would be another day. Add to the cost of the police officers the cost of the deputy district attorneys that had to prepare and process these . . . cases. Add the cost of the salaries of the Public Defender's office to defend them; the costs of the salaries of the judges and the juries to hear the cases, and the costs that also go along with running a court. The cost of the clerk and the reporter. There is no doubt in my mind that the cost is staggering.

I have spoken with numerous narcotics officers, and they have the same opinion that I have: that the effectiveness is almost nil. We are barely scratching the surface. For every arrest that takes place, there may be 1,000 or 2,000 other people that are using marijuana.

There is no way for me to prove this. The only instance that I can cite to you is the manner in which most of these arrests take place. These arrests take place, for the most part, by accident. They are not arrests where the police are going out looking for marijuana. That does happen. But the majority of arrests are by accident. A person is driving an automobile, and he goes through a red light. The police give him a ticket, and they notice a marijuana cigarette in an ashtray. Then, two hours of time are taken in processing the individual. Or, somebody is shot, and he is rushed to the hospital and prepared for surgery and a marijuana cigarette falls out of his shirt. There is no question in my mind that most of the arrests occur in this fashion.

While arguing that the cost of enforcement is high and the effect "minimal" Reichman does state he feels these factors should not be the guiding points that determine whether or not existing laws should be changed. In testimony, his primary interest was directed toward the question of whether or not the use of the drug had any relationship to subsequent crimes. Reflecting on the high cost of alcoholism and its relationship to crime, Mr. Reichman states, on the basis of his experience, he sincerely doubts "that the use of marijuana plays a vital factor in the commission of other crimes."

Aiming his guns at the current laws, Reichman specifically criticized the manner in which most cases had to be handled in California (and in most other states) when an offender is brought to trial.

> A man can go out and steal a car and receive a misdemeanor sentence, and a man can go out and commit an assault with a deadly weapon and receive a misdemeanor sentence, but a man that is smoking one marijuana cigarette, he is going to receive a felony. [Reichman notes that] there is a world of difference between someone that possesses three or four kilos of marijuana, and somebody that possesses one marijuana cigarette. I feel that the court should be given discretion to impose misdemeanor sentences in marijuana cases if they so desire [yet] a person convicted of possessing marijuana cannot receive a misdemeanor sentence. Ethically, I think such a change [i.e., giving the court misdemeanor discretion] will, somewhat, reduce the costs. I have no doubt that many of our marijuana cases go to trial because the defendant, who was caught with one or two marijuana cigarettes, doesn't want to have this stigma of a felony facing him for the rest of his life. And if there was this misdemeanor alternative, I think many of the cases would terminate in a plea.

In summary, Reichman suggested that if the legislature really wanted to handle the situation correctly they "should give serious consideration to treating marijuana violations the same way that alcohol violations are concerned. It is my feeling," he said, "that the marijuana law is just like any other criminal law, whether it is marijuana, whether it is a traffic violation. It is a problem of balancing the interests. On the one hand, the interest of the individual to a freedom of choice and, on the other hand, the interests of society to protect itself."

And in conclusion the Deputy District Attorney had this to

say: "I want to add one thing here. I don't smoke marijuana. I don't urge people to smoke it. On the contrary, I urge people not to smoke it. . . . I don't want my remarks to be misconstrued. Regardless of what is done, it should still be made a crime to furnish marijuana to juveniles. It should still be made a crime to drive an automobile under the influence of marijuana."

Wilbur F. Littlefield,[26] chief trial deputy of the Public Defender's Office in Los Angeles, had this to say in regard to Reichman's testimony:

> I agree . . . that there should be an alternative sentence•so far as the first offender on possession of marijuana is concerned. . . . I practised law when we did have an alternative sentence for possession of marijuana . . . and it was my experience during that period, that it was much more likely that a defendant would plead guilty. If he has a straight felony, as the law is at the present time, facing him, certainly he has nothing whatsoever to gain [in pleading guilty] even if he is given probation with proceedings suspended and no time whatsoever in jail. He is still a convicted felon.
>
> And considering the youthfulness of many of our persons who are charged with possession of marijuana . . . many of them are between the ages of 18 and 21 and they don't realize what the seriousness of a felony conviction can mean ten or fifteen years after the conviction. . . . I think we have made a great mistake in California in taking the discretion completely away from the court as we have in marijuana offenses, so far as sentencing is concerned." But Littlefield also saw fit to add this comment: "It is not the position of our office to say that marijuana should be legalized. We don't believe that it should be. But, we do believe that the penalties for possession of marijuana should be reduced.

If there are those among state legislators and law enforcement personnel who advocate modification of the marijuana laws, especially with an eye toward reducing the severity of sentences for youthful first offenders, there are those of the pro-cannabis lobby who press for complete repeal. On July 24, 1967, for instance, the *London Times* carried a full-page advertisement instigated by American psychologist Stephen Abrams, which bore the headline, "The law against marijuana is immoral in principle and unworkable in practice." The ad carried endorsement signatures of some sixty-five prominent Britishers and introduced its arguments with a quotation by Spinoza:

> All laws which can be violated without doing anyone any injury are laughed at. Nay, so far are they from doing anything to control the desires and passions of man that, on the contrary, they direct and incite men's thoughts toward those very objects; for we always strive toward what is forbidden and desire the things we are not allowed to have. And men of leisure are never deficient in the ingenuity needed to enable them to outwit laws framed to regulate things which cannot be entirely forbidden. . . . He who tries to determine everything by law will foment crime rather than lessen it.

It is, of course, extremely difficult to legislate moral conduct. Barry Goldwater emphasized this point during the 1964 presidential campaign, and he added: "I propose to extend freedom. My aim is not to pass laws, but to repeal them. It is not to inaugurate new programs but to cancel old ones that do violence to the Constitution, or that have failed in their purpose." Antoni Gollan uses this Goldwater quotation to expand on his point that the marijuana laws have failed and should be repealed. But Ferdinand Mount replies:

> Sweep away the prohibition and you sweep away the racketeering? Not so. Britain abolished most of her legal restraints on betting and gaming (the parallel with Prohibition and its repeal was made during the passage of this legislation too), and what happened? The British embarked on an orgy of gambling such as was never seen before. Millionaires and workingmen ruined themselves, and the gangsters moved in, not out. Gangland killings erupted and the American Mafia even started hotfooting it across the Atlantic. Nor, to put it mildly, is racketeering less in evidence in states where gambling is legal and liquor easy to get than in those where they are not. It is obvious that if marijuana were legal more people would smoke it. More people would therefore be aware of the delights of taking leave of their senses. Anybody who claims that there would then be *fewer* people ready to go on to experiment with heroin is operating with an exiguous knowledge of human nature. Did the end of Prohibition bring a significant or lasting reduction in alcoholism?

Perhaps current legislation against users is too strong. Yet, while recognizing this, prominent authorities who have to work with this problem urge caution in becoming too lax in permitting the use of the drug. Possession in California at the time of this writing, although it may soon be changed, now demands a felony sentence. This is mandatory; the judge has no discretion in the matter. Some judges are reluctant to give a felony record to a young first-time offender. Even if the judge suspends the sentence, the record of the defendant will still retain the felony conviction with all the detrimental effects that can accrue to the holder.

In a preliminary position paper concerning the point[27] California lawmen said this: "That the narcotic marijuana is a harmful and destructive substance is not open to question or debate by reasonable individuals." On the other hand, the paper noted some judges may exhibit reluctance to convict defendants on a first-time charge of possession with the result that this has "led to a diminution of our ability to effectively enforce the law." The lawmen expressed the hope that giving judges discretion to fix the degree of the crime as that of a misdemeanor in certain deserving cases will cause them to give "more realistic" disposition of marijuana possession cases.

Where marijuana is concerned it is one thing to quote arguments against bad laws and quite another to ascertain for certain that the laws against marijuana are, indeed, bad. What must be determined is whether or not the problems produced by cannabis are sufficiently dangerous to society so that a stiff penalty deterrent is necessary to force and persuade people from resorting to enjoying the euphoriant effects of cannabis.

Two relatively minor changes in federal law took place on May 19, 1969, when the United States Supreme Court overturned the conviction of Timothy Leary under two clauses of the Federal Marijuana Tax Law. Leary's comments on this occasion were less than accurate. "The facts of the matter," he said, "are that today there are no federal laws against marijuana."[27a] This is not true. The laws which were held invalid were relatively narrow ones concerned with the presumption that a person carrying marijuana across a border was importing it illegally and knew that the importation was illegal. Federal laws concerned with possession and illegal importation itself still exist. Moreover, most marijuana arrests are made in accordance with state laws against use and possession, and these laws are all still in force.

THE FUTURE OF CANNABIS

If it were possible to control the effects of dangerous drugs to the point where they could not alter the behavior or perception of the user we would have no need for restrictive or punitive drug laws. Unfortunately, society has never been able to protect the individual or his neighbors from the results of the user's lack of interest in, or capability of, limiting his intake of drugs once he becomes dependent on them and thus avoid the point where intoxication makes him a menace. As a result, we have resorted to a poor and not always effective method of control. We pass restrictive and punitive laws hoping we can maintain the balance between the individual's rights and his responsibilities. Where drug laws are concerned we try to protect the majority from drug abuse and its effects by a minority, particularly where such abuse can result in violence, death, and the acting out of antisocial impulses.

Moreover, through our laws, we hope to prevent drug-induced indolence, incompetence, unemployment, and the whole train of pathetic events secondary to drug abuse which increase the burden on the majority to support an irresponsible, unproductive, drug-dependent minority. For it has been amply demonstrated that when drug-seeking behavior and drug abuse become the major goals of the individual he becomes a drain on society.

The problem is that in our zeal we have in some areas permitted and promoted laws that are disproportionately severe to the crime involved. Once these laws are on the books and it becomes necessary for enforcement officials to arrest and for courts to condemn, the general public complains that this wasn't the way it was meant to be. This has been particularly true in recent years when the cannabis laws as a specific example have begun to pinch the average middle- and upper-class American family. Along with the complaints about the laws have come recriminations of police and courts that were only carrying out the expressed will of the voters through the action of their legislators.

In effect, the problem today is, do we or don't we want individuals smoking cannabis? Can we or can't we afford economically, socially, and individually to repeat the expensive experiments performed inadvertently in other nations throughout history where the drug got out of control? With alcohol firmly entrenched in the American way of life and with all the sorrow it brings, can we afford to legalize another habit that has at least equal, if not greater, potential of causing national harm? The problem, says the sociologist, is that "since the smoking of marijuana will undoubtedly continue regardless of legislation against it, it can also be argued that it would be better to accept the inevitable than to wage war for a lost cause."[28] In offering this solution he again equates the drug with alcohol and suggests we treat the marijuana problem in the same manner. The problem, however, is that we have never really dealt with the alcohol problem. We have only contended with it. And we continue to contend with it despite the fact that alcohol abuse constitutes the major drug abuse problem in the United States today.

When we repealed the Volstead Act the 96 percent of Americans who wanted to enjoy alcohol socially decided their needs were more important than the abuse problems that continued to arise from the misadventures of the remaining 4 percent. The financial profit that has accrued to the few as a result of this decision and the emotional satisfaction that has accrued to many have not yet counterbalanced the economic and social toll this habit has placed upon the nation.

Certainly there is wisdom in the statement of the President's Ad Hoc Panel on Drug Abuse when in 1962[29] it stated: "It is the opinion of the panel that the hazards of marijuana per se have been exaggerated and that long criminal sentences imposed on an occasional user or possessor of the drug are in poor social perspective." Yet, the panel recognized the need for laws in controlling the abusive use of all dangerous drugs. If we are to have these laws and if they are to be effective, they must have sufficient teeth to make it feasible and reasonable for enforcement officers to risk their lives in an attempt to fulfill the intent of these laws. If the law has no negative

152

alternative to offer the abuser, the law will have no effect. In such cases the law would better have not been written.

It might be well, before we exceed the intent of the recommendation of the President's Ad Hoc Panel and throw open the floodgates of approval to all who might wish to use cannabis, to consider a comment made by our nation's sixteenth President. Noting that destruction of our nation could not come from abroad, President Lincoln commented:[30] "If destruction be our lot, we ourselves must be its author and finisher. As a nation of free men, we must live through all times, or die by suicide." Although Lincoln had no reference to drug abuse when he made this statement, he nonetheless painted a clear picture of how drug abuse can become a national menace—a menace that clouds men's minds and deludes their thoughts. To date, no more effective method for controlling men has been devised than the process by which men permit themselves to be smothered by the effects of dangerous drugs. The victor in the struggle against such loss of reason must be the man who can keep his mind clear. Today, then, the struggle for the moderate use of drugs is aimed at the control of men's minds.

The time in history has come to make the decision as to what we want to do with cannabis. As we do, it might be well to remember that, while drugs can offer us escape through illusion and give us pleasure through euphoria, there is only one way of life that can give us happiness: facing, living in, and coping with reality on our own without a pharmacologic crutch. If we come to the point where we cannot do this, the battle is done and drug abuse will be the victor.

1. John Rosevear, *Pot: A Handbook of Marijuana* (New York: University Books, 1967), p. 122.

2. *Ibid.*, p. 124.

3. *Ibid.*, p. 126.

4. *Ibid.*, p. 117.

5. *Ibid.*, p. 104.

6. *Ibid.*, p. 95.

7. *People of Colorado vs. David H. Stark* (1965), 400 P. 2d., 923, No. 21394.

8. "Marijuana: Millions of Turned-on Users," *Life*, July 7, 1967, pp. 16-23.

9. John Glenn, "Narcotics Conviction Can Hurt Job Chances

Students Warned," *Los Angeles Times,* Nov. 29, 1967.

10. Lloyd Shearer, "Why Students Take Pot," *Parade,* Oct. 15, 1967.

11. George B. McClellan, "Canada's mounties: Focus on a famous force," *Pace* 2(1): 41 (Feb., 1966).

12. *Holland vs. Missouri,* 252 US 416, 1920.

13. *Single Convention on Narcotic Drugs of the United Nations, 1961,* art. 28, par. 1; art. 49, par. 2(f).

14. Boris Yaro, "Legalize Marijuana for Adults, Judge Urges," *Los Angeles Times,* Sept. 24, 1967.

15. Rudy Villasenor, "Judge Who Urged Legal Marijuana Relieved of Post, " *Los Angeles Times,* Oct. 5, 1967.

16. Donald Louria, *Nightmare Drugs* (New York: Pocket Books, 1966), p. 36.

17. Gene R. Haislip, "Current Issues in the Prevention and Control of Marijuana Abuse," paper presented to the First National Conference on Student Drug Involvement at the University of Maryland, Aug. 16, 1967.

18. Ferdinand Mount, "The Wild Grass Chase," *National Review,* Jan. 20, 1968, p. 84.

19. Jerry Cohen, "Marijuana: Views Collide," *Los Angeles Times,* Dec. 4, 1967.

20. Antoni Gollan, "The Great Marijuana Problem," *National Review,* Jan. 20, 1968, p. 75.

21. Joseph Oteri, quoted by Cohen, *op. cit.*

22. *Commonwealth of Massachusetts vs. Joseph D. Leis and Ivan Weiss,* Superior Court Nos. 28841-2, 28844-5, and 28864-5.

23. Mount, *op. cit.*

24. Pete Wilson, "Juvenile Drug Abuse as a Legislative Problem" (unpublished paper).

25. Joe Reichman, testimony given before the Senate Public Health and Safety Committee, Los Angeles, California, Oct. 18, 1967.

26. Wilbur F. Littlefield, *ibid.*

27. Gene Blake, "Peace Officers and DAs Back Bill on Marijuana," *Los Angeles Times,* April 16, 1968.

27a. "Leary Tosses Head into the Ring," *Los Angeles Free Press* (May 23, 1969), p. 2.

28. Alfred Lindesmith, *The Addict and the Law* (Bloomington: Indiana University Press, 1965), p. 241.

29. *Proceedings, White House Conference on Narcotic and Drug Abuse* (Washington, D.C.: U.S. Government Printing Office, 1962), p. 286.

30. Abraham Lincoln, address before the Young Men's Lyceum, Springfield, Ill., Jan. 27, 1838.

POTPOURRI

The following list does not aim to be an exhaustive glossary but is confined to those terms directly related to the use of drugs. Since the special language of the drug subculture constantly changes, some of these terms may already be passing out of currency as new ones come in; but a great many of them have endured for many years and give prospect of continuing in use for a long time.

Acid	Lysergic acid diethylamide (LSD), a powerful hallucinogenic substance that was at one time the mainstay of the psychedelic drug users and was used as a medium for obtaining very high intoxications and unpredictable psychological excursions.
At	Where drug action is taking place.
Backwards	A term applied to tranquilizers.
Bag	One's particular interest or attachment; if one is attracted to cannabis, then cannabis is his bag, and so on.
Ball	A pleasant happening. The term may refer either to events in general or to a sexual experience.
Babysit	To guide a person through his drug experience. Babysitters are usually experienced drug users.
Be-in	A collection of people meeting for some specific purpose. Usually this term applies to hippie conclaves or at least to assemblies of "in" people who gather for various activities.
Benny	The term may refer to any amphetamine, but specifically denotes amphetamine sulfate or phosphate. Obese people take these to lose weight, since bennies tend to depress appetite. Drug users take them to promote alertness and for various types of drug trips. The latter experiences are usually followed by depression.

155

	If used chronically, bennies may cause physical and mental deterioration.
Blow	1) to leave willingly.
	2) to invite to leave, usually because of disapproval of one's conduct.
	3) to perform well, either verbally or musically.
Blow one's mind	On the positive side this may be an astonishing or fascinating experience; on the negative, it may denote a bad trip or an experience that causes one to become upset or depressed.
Boo	Cannabis.
Boo Hoo	A "priest" in the hippie Neo American Church.
Boss	Originally a surfing term. Roughly synonymous with "groovy."
Blue Devils	Amobarbital capsules.
Blue Fascists	One of the milder synonyms for the police.
Bread	Money, usually a large sum in contrast to "crumbs," which means change or small bills.
Bug	To bother or pester someone.
Bum trip	A bad experience; usually used in connection with the use of mind-affecting drugs, but also employed to describe any emotional experience that was depressing or disturbing.
Bummer	A bad trip.
Burned	Used to describe the acquisition of bad drugs, diluted drugs, or no drugs at all, even though cash has been exchanged.
Bust	An arrest. Usually this implies that the police have descended upon a gathering and rounded the participants up for questioning or arrest.
Busted	Arrested, specifically for drugs, but also for any other criminal activity.
Cache	*See* Stash.
Can	One ounce of marijuana; a lid.
Cannabis	The genus name for all the tetrahydrocannabinol-producing weeds.
Carrying	Transporting drugs or keeping them on one's person while in transit; *see* Holding.
Changes	Emotional swings and variations, particularly those experienced while on drugs.
Cat	An informed person who knows where the action is; usually said of the male; *see* Chick.
Chalk	Methamphetamine.
Chick	A sexually desirable young female.

Chip	To play around with a drug; to use drugs sporadically.
Chipper	One who chips.
Coke	Cocaine.
Connection	1) The source of illegal drugs, usually a seller.
	2) A source who can direct one to a seller but who may not sell himself.
	3) A person who gives or sells information.
Contact	1) To meet someone to buy drugs.
	2) The man who sells drugs or directs one to a seller.
	3) A source for drugs.
Contact high	A trip caused by the emotional experience of observing or being near someone who is high because of actual drug indulgence. The idea is the same as the empathetic response occurring when one sees another yawn.
Cool	1) In tune with what's happening. Also refers to being unusually adept in moving within the drug scene and coping with its problems.
	2) All right, safe.
Cop	1) Police.
	2) To buy or obtain drugs.
	3) To steal.
Cop out	1) *See* Fink.
	2) To drop out of the drug world and return to the world of the Establishment.
	3) To give up.
Co-pilots	Amphetamines.
Cope	To maintain while intoxicated on drugs, i.e., to handle oneself effectively while under the influence of drugs. This ability varies from person to person and takes practice to acquire.
Crash	1) To fall asleep; may be said for those who are up on drugs but also denotes any sudden falling asleep.
	2) A comedown from a drug episode, usually a precipitous and unpleasant one; for example, crashing in the middle of a drug episode because of an arrest.
Crashpad	A place to sleep.
Crazy	1) Exciting, in the know, enjoyable.
	2) A general term of approval, especially of happenings in the drug world which are pre-

	sumed to be annoying to the establishment.
Crumbs	Money, but in small amounts. *See* Bread.
Crutch	1) An aid (e.g., drugs) one must have to cope with daily existence.
	2) A split match which is used as a roach holder.
Cut out	To leave, depart.
Dealer	A heavy supplier of illegal drugs. Also called the "man," or the "connection."
Dexies	Dextroamphetamine sulfate (a mixture of barbiturate and amphetamine).
Dig	To understand, usually to appreciate, approve, or enjoy.
Digger	A hippie father figure who tries to obtain beds, food, money, or employment for needy hippies.
Dime bag	Ten dollars worth of drugs, usually cannabis.
Doing	May be any "happening," but specifically the taking of a drug.
Doing one's own thing	Indulging in one's "bag"; participating in action notably pleasurable to the doer.
Dope	1) To drug or give any drugs to a person.
	2) Specifically, opiates and opiate narcotics.
	3) A synonym for glue used for glue-sniffing.
	4) Occasionally used to describe any drug.
Downer	1) A down trip, a bummer, a bad drug experience.
	2) A synonym for depressant drugs such as barbiturates.
Drag	A boring happening, a meaningless situation.
Dreamer	1) morphine or opiate narcotics.
	2) One who takes opiates.
Drop out	1) One who withdraws from society or dispenses with its social mores.
	2) The ultimate happening in the psychedelic experience. The term is used both as a noun to denote the doer and as a verb to describe the experience.
Dynamite	Boss, groovy, especially in discussing the effects of cannabis, i.e. "This weed is dynamite."
Establishment	People over the age of 30 (or, generously, 35), usually straight, more often square.
Far out	1) Authentically bizarre.
	2) Avant garde, new, unusual.
Fed	A federal narcotics agent.

158

Fix	A shot of drugs, usually heroin, but also applied to speed.
Fink	To give information, usually to the establishment.
Flip	To express unusually strong emotion that may range from untoward enthusiasm to psychotic behavior.
Footballs	Amphetamines.
Forwards	Pep pills, specifically amphetamines; *see* Backwards.
Freak	1) One who has flipped, i.e., one who uses drugs to the point of transcending reality. 2) Used to describe a special type of intense abuser of a particular psychedelic drug, such as "speed freak," or "acid freak."
Freak out	Truly to loose all contact with reality.
Fuzz	The police.
Game	An unnecessary type of behavior designed to impress others.
Get into something	To enter into the action, to be involved.
Giggle-smoke	Cannabis, or cannabis smoke.
Go	1) To swing, to participate freely in the drug scene. 2) To perform unusually well. 3) Used as a shout of encouragement.
Going up	Taking drugs to obtain their effect; said of smoking cannabis or injecting speed, etc.
Goof balls	Barbiturates.
Grass	Cannabis
Grass Brownies	Cookies containing cannabis.
Griffo	Cannabis.
Groove	To concentrate intensely on an object or activity, usually with pleasure.
Groovy	An enjoyable activity or person; swinging; with it.
Groover	One who grooves.
Guide	One who babysits a novice when he goes up on a psychedelic substance; *see* Babysitter.
Hallucinogens	Psychotoxic drugs that affect the mind in such a way as to produce sensations that are distorted and abnormal in content. The term is strictly establishment in that users normally deny that drugs such as LSD actually produce

	psychotic or pseudo-psychotic episodes.
Hangup	A habit or idea which causes one discomfort; *see also* Hung up.
Happening	Action; what's occurring at the moment of interest to the drug group. An exciting or pleasurable event.
Hashish	Resin from the *Cannabis indica* plant which contains a very high THC content.
Hassle	1) An argument or unpleasant discourse between people. 2) Any unpleasant situation or duty which disrupts the tranquility of doing one's own thing.
Head	A chronic user of a drug or drugs, e.g., pothead, acid head, etc. Within the drug subculture this term is identifying only; within the establishment it is identifying and derogatory.
Hearts	Amphetamines, specifically dextroamphetamine and benzedrine sulfate.
Heat	Police.
H	Heroin.
High	Being intoxicated, turned on, exhilarated, particularly by the use of drugs such as cannabis.
Hip	Aware, in the know, informed.
Hit	1) An arrest. 2) To smoke a joint of marijuana.
Hold	To keep cannabis or other drugs on one's person for use, transit, or sale. One may also hold by storing drugs in his house; *see* Carrying.
Horse	Heroin.
Hung up	Trapped in a snare of emotional, psychological, or interpersonal problems that prevent one from enjoying drugs or life in general.
Hustle	To precipitate a happening of any kind.
Hype	One who uses intravenous drugs, specifically heroin or speed.
Ice Cream Habit	Sporadic use of drugs; *see* Chip.
Indian Hay	Cannabis, specifically *Cannabis indica,* or hashish.
Joint	1) A marijuana cigarette. 2) A place where the action is.
Junk	Heroin.
Junkie	Heroin user.
Key	*See* Kilo.

Kilo	2.2 pounds of drug substance, almost always cannabis. Usually this amount is compressed into brick form for transport.
Lame ones	Those who need a crutch to cope with reality.
Lard	Police.
Let it all hang out	To give the facts, to hide nothing.
Lid	Approximately an ounce of marijuana; also called a can.
Love-in	A be-in dedicated to peace and love and, on occasion, cannabis smoking and sex.
LSD-25	Lysergic acid diethylamide, derived originally from rye ergot. It was discovered in 1943 by Hoffman, kept a relative secret until recent years when it became the "sacrament" of the hippies. At the time of this writing it is not manufactured legally in the United Staes.
Man	1) A drug connection. 2) The police. 3) A term of address within the drug group, e.g., 'Hey there, man!"
Marijuana	Cannabis, usually *Cannabis americana* or *mexicana*. Specifically, the flowering tops of the female plant which contain the majority of the plant's THC content.
Mary Jane	Cannabis.
Matchbox	A small amount of cannabis sufficient to make between five to eight cigarettes; about a fifth of a lid.
Meth	Methamphetamine; *see* Speed.
Mindblower	An experience or a drug which upsets one's emotional and/or psychological equilibrium.
Mohasky	Cannabis.
Mu	Cannabis.
Muggles	Cannabis.
Narc	A narcotics agent.
Nickel bag	A five-dollar quantity of cannabis which usually makes between five and eight joints.
Out of it	Not in contact, not part of the drug scene.
Out of sight	Tremendous, superb, so good it can't be believed.
Pad	One's living quarters.
Panama Red	A potent type of South American cannabis.
Pep Pills	Stimulants, specifically amphetamines.

161

Poke	A puff on a joint.
Pot	Cannabis.
Pot Likker	Cannabis tea, usually made with regular tea boiled with cannabis leaves.
Pothead	A chronic cannabis user.
Psychedelic	That which enhances or expands consciousness.
Push	1) To sell, specifically narcotics and dangerous drugs. 2) To attempt to manipulate one's environment or to encourage things to happen.
Rap	To communicate peacefully and/or with purpose.
Red Birds	Secobarbital capsules.
Reefer	A joint, a marijuana cigarette.
Ripped	Highly intoxicated on drugs.
Roach	The butt end of a marijuana cigarette which contains a high THC content that accumulates as the cigarette is burned.
Roach Holder	A device that enables the smoker to hold a joint so it can be consumed to the very end. Often these holders are elaborate, jeweled items, but they may be made of broom straws or match sticks.
Scene	The place where the action is, as well as all that is happening at the time. Similar to the scene of a play which portrays all the events of the moment.
Score	1) The important facts about a given event or subject. 2) To buy or acquire drugs or sex. 3) To acquire recognition for an accomplishment.
Smashed	Intoxicated; *see* stoned.
Smoke	Cannabis (Particularly on the East Coast).
Snow	Cocaine.
Sock it to me	1) To tell the straight facts, to speak plainly and honestly. 2) Sexually, the term denotes assent on the part of the speaker for mutual participation.
Space out	In a daze, particularly a daze resulting from a trip due to the use of psychotoxins.
Speed	Stimulants, specifically methamphetamine (desoxyephedrine), a drug capable of producing intense highs with, in most cases, subsequent

	severe crashes.
Splash	Speed.
Square	Not with it, straight-laced, narrow-minded, un-imaginative, anti-hip.
Stash	A secret supply of drugs, a cache.
Stoned	Very high on drugs, usually to the point of being unable to cope with reality.
Straight	1) One who does not use drugs. 2) More broadly, one who is not connected with the drug or swinging sex world. This is not usually a derogatory term but is used to identify one's social association in contrast to the word "square," which is not a complimentary term.
Stuff	Cannabis or other drugs.
Swing	To be an active and effective participant in the action or happening in the drug and/or the liberal sexual world.
Swinger	One who is an active participant in the drug world.
Tea	Cannabis.
Tell it like it is	(or tell it the way it is) To tell the truth without embellishment.
Tetrahydrocannabinols	Identified as the group of substances which are responsible for the psychotoxicity and other pharmacological effects that accrue from the use of cannabis.
THC	Tetrahydrocannabinol.
Tighten up	To turn on, to smoke cannabis.
Toke	To smoke a marijuana cigarette.
Toke up	1) To drag on a cannabis-filled cigarette or pipe. 2) To go up significantly on cannabis.
Torn up	Intoxicated, stoned.
Trip	An emotional excursion into unknown psychological realms involving heightened sensual perception and concentraiton. In drug parlance this is the result of taking drugs and obtaining their effects.
Trip out	1) To immerse oneself in a happening. 2) To become intensely involved.
Turn off	To dispel interest, to bore, to cause indifference.

Turn on	1) In the limited sense, to smoke marijuana or take another hallucinogen.
	2) In the general sense, to acquire expanded appreciation of an event or experience as a result of being highly pleased by it.
	3) To come alive, to enter the drug society.
	4) To imply that one has encouraged another to use a drug.
Tuned in	1) To become markedly aware of oneself as a result of mind expansion due to drug use.
	2) Generally, to be aware of the scene and usually part of it.
Uncool	One who is aware but incapable (because of hangups or comparable problems) of participating fully in the action. An uncool person may endanger a cool scene because of his lack of self-control and inability to maintain. This is a most uncomplimentary term.
Underground	This is the whole drug subculture, its inhabitants, its activities, its philosophies.
Up	To be under the influence of a drug. Usually not in full control of oneself. The person who is "up" is usually sympathetically protected by others in the drug commmutity until he comes down.
Uppers	Stimulants.
Up tight	Nervous, anxious, tense.
Weed	Cannabis.
Where it's at	The place, real or imagined, where the action is. To know "where it's at" is to be aware of the drug scene.
Wig	One's mind.
Wig out	To blow one's mind.
Yellow Jackets	Pentobarbital capsules.
Zig-zag	Roll-your-own cigarette paper.

"One of these days, Dr. Leary will go too far."

ЯPPENÐIX

In the body of this book we discussed the major controversies surrounding the use of cannabis—those concerning cannabis and alcohol and cannabis and tobacco on the pro-cannabis side, and those concerning cannabis and crime and cannabis and violence on the anti-cannabis side. These by no means exhaust all of the issues and problems associated with the use of marijuana, and indeed many other issues have been touched on in the book. Certain questions however, are repeatedly raised: the relation of cannabis to "religions" that claim cannabis as a sacrament, the use or excuse of the use of cannabis by prominent people, the connection of cannabis with more dangerous drugs, and many, many more. Such questions have been gathered here in question and answer form. For the most part the questions are phrased from the pro-cannabis side, as though they were being posed by those who have used or would like to try cannabis. The answers, although tending to discourage cannabis use are, above all, attempts to present such facts as are known in each case. We hope the reader will find the questions, and the answers, he is looking for.

Isn't pot the "in" thing today. Aren't all the "cool" kids using pot?

Not really. Although statistics will vary from study to study, the actual number of true *users* is relatively small. Users in this sense, however, have to be defined differently from those who play occasionally. The users and players are noisy about their habit and attract attention and publicity that causes many to believe their number is much greater than it actually is. Additionally, because they feel that current cannabis legislation is an intrusion on their friends' personal liberties, many nonusers join the crusade. This combination tends to help swell the continuing flood of publicity which, in truth, causes others to try the drug out of curiosity.

Some journalists have not been helpful in presenting an unbiased picture of cannabis use in this country. The "guesstimate"[1] of health officials in Washington may be correct that twenty million Americans have tried cannabis. But trying it and chronically using it are two different things. In the recent headlines about thirteen midshipmen at the Naval Academy in Annapolis who were dismissed because they were "using" cannabis, the fact was obscured that half of these men were single-time users who tried it from peer pressure or out of curiosity. At about the same time the Academy situation came to light, Ithaca College in New York State polled its two thousand students regarding their use of cannabis. Twenty-two percent had tried it, but only 15 percent had used it on more than two occasions. Only 3 percent of the student body had ever tried other psychedelic drugs.

As for the appeal of fashion, the arguments against it are as old as the study of ethics. Anyone who believes that fashion should be followed simply because it is fashion is in need of guidance counseling or a solid course in philosophy.

Aren't all sorts of really intelligent people using cannabis? I can give you names of doctors and lawyers and ministers and teachers, not to mention top students, who use it without any harm.

Of course. In rebuttal, consider the following from Los Angeles Judge Arthur Alarcon: "It is my opinion that marijuana use, especially among college students and their pseudo-intellectual leaders from the professional ranks is a symptom and not the cause of preexisting profound psychological disturbance which is magnified by marijuana."[2]

There are, to be sure, a number of people who can use marijuana at frequent intervals and not be impaired by the drug's effects. This should not be surprising, knowing as we do the tremendous variables involved in the use of cannabis. The effects of consuming cannabis, note Drs. David Maurer and Victor Vogel,[3] "differ widely with the culture, with different racial stocks, with various religious groups, and with varying social status of the individuals who consume it. Furthermore, hemp raised in different parts of the world, while consistent in producing the essential cannabinol or intoxicating principle, varies widely in the content and strength of the drug produced; soil, climate, light intensity, latitude, etc., have a profound effect on the hemp plant. Also, the effects vary widely with the part of the plant consumed, and with various methods of consumption."

The end result of this tremendous variability is that, first, we cannot predict just what will occur when a given person takes the drug, because mood, ideation, inclination, external stimuli, and other variables influence the outcome. Second, it can be assumed that while much of the time the use of milder forms of cannabis available in this country will not produce adverse effects, we are not sure this will always be the case, or that the milder forms will not give way to stronger ones as use spreads.

As for the "top students" of cannabis legend, Yale psychologist Kenneth Kenniston[4] states that these users are "a small but talented minority. They are generally very bright, hard-working students who maintain A and B averages." But these users are not dependent upon cannabis in the true sense of the word. They are "chippers" and lack the addict's compulsive need to relieve intolerable tension and depression. Unlike the true addict they remain in the mainstream of life despite, not because of, their use of the drug. They continue to be achievement-oriented and competitive. The true problem presented by this small minority is that by example they encourage others to try marijuana who may lack their stability and drive. The results can be disastrous. There may even be some naïve enough to imagine that cannabis will *help* them to get good grades; but that's being very naïve indeed.

It should be clear, then, that marijuana use is a kind of chemical Russian roulette. The risk is great. Because one person spins the revolver and comes up with a blank is no guarantee that the next one will be so fortunate. Those who do become dependent on the drug resemble one another enough so that their emotional characteristics and behavior patterns can largely be predicted, and the description of such persons often fits, not the top students, but the dropouts.

Commenting on young Moroccan kif (cannabis) users, Benabud[5] notes they are immature young people who exhibit a prevalence of the imaginary over the real; they prefer today instead of worrying about the future; they demonstrate a compulsive need to satisfy their desires right now and are frustrated if they cannot. He concludes from this that some users are more or less destined to become addicted to kif because of an emotional predisposition that makes the effects of the drug attractive to them. This, he says, justifies an old Moroccan saying that "You are a kif addict long before you smoke your first pipe." The sad thing is that most of these future addicts are unaware of the impending danger. Their psychological predisposition to respond positively to the effects of the drug is so strong that one exposure, one puff, starts them on the road to drug oblivion.

Maybe it's true that some of these professional people have problems, just as young people do, but if they can smoke cannabis why shouldn't young people? It is true, isn't it, that some highly placed people really do smoke cannabis?

Yes, some of them do. To deny this would be less than honest. But let's take a closer look at the adults who use marijuana in the tightly guarded privacy of their homes or offices.

One of the more damaging of these episodes happened in a small northern California town in 1967. None of the principals, least of all the central figure, ever thought they would come to public attention. The case in point involved one of the more prominent citizens who lived near the little three-room schoolhouse that served the children of the area. The citizen: Mrs. Garnett Brennan, a cheerful, wide-eyed, blithe spirit who, as an accredited California teacher for thirty years, was serving as the teaching principal of the town's elementary school.

Nearing age sixty, Mrs. Brennan was recently fired from her job because she signed an affidavit to help a young friend who was arrested for selling marijuana. In this affidavit she stated she knew cannabis was not harmful because she had smoked it almost daily herself for nearly eighteen years. The experience, she said, was quite beneficial, relaxing, and a great aid in staying up late to correct papers. Discreet Mrs. Brennan never smoked in public, only at home. In public she used tobacco, which she recently affirmed she wished she could quit.

According to *Life* magazine writer Shana Alexander,[6] Mrs. Brennan began her habit in 1947 when she was visiting at Big Sur, California, now famed as a hippie mecca. "I remember the first time someone turned me on back there," the teacher told the columnist, "I felt just like Alice in Wonderland. I'd stand up and grow taller and taller. I'd reach out my arm and watch it grow longer and longer. I wondered why I didn't fall into the Pacific Ocean. Then I thought: how crazy reading is. . . ."

Things are no longer the same for Mrs. Brennan. The tiny zinnia bed where she grew her own supply of cannabis fails to sprout her plants now, by law. She no longer uses cannabis, having renounced it until "it becomes legal," chiefly to prove that she can give it up. She is not now in charge of the school; she was fired when her use of cannabis became public knowledge.

It happens that Mrs. Brennan was but one of nearly two thousand solid citizens living in the San Francisco area who came to the aid of the young man facing a jail sentence for selling cannabis. The signers of the petition were warned ahead of time by their attorneys that they did not have to say they personally smoked marijuana; all they had to do was certify from firsthand experience or observation that they knew it was not a dangerous drug. Even this testimony might place them in jeopardy. Mrs. Brennan thought it over and said to herself, "Shoot, it's no worse than having to be cool all the time. So," she continued, "we all took our copies home from the court and that night I got high and wrote mine out." The affidavits were given to the judge in San Francisco at 2 P.M. that fateful Friday. Less than an hour later the administrative axe fell.

"She didn't intend to play Snow White," Miss Alexander reflects in her story, "only to help a friend in trouble. She did not even anticipate that her endorsement of pot would ever be made public. At such naïveté I am moved to say, 'Wow.' "

Now, let us see what can be culled from this unfortunate experience. First, it is obvious that stable, intelligent, capable, socially valuable people can use cannabis and that such use can be maintained for long periods of time by these people without any visible adverse effects. It would be a mistake to assume that such practice is commonplace, but it obviously occurs. But let's consider another point. Mrs. Brennan did not sign her devastating affidavit while she had good control of her reasoning power. By her own testimony she took the affidavit home and "that night . . . got high" and wrote it out. For years her common sense kept her from discovery. Then, one night, the very drug she was defending tripped her up and destroyed her career. Had she remained cool and thought the situation over when the haze of the cannabis smoke had blown away, she might well still be teaching school.

Mrs. Brennan got by with using the drug over a long period of time. Most do not. Some will either become dependent on it or go on to something stronger. Most will give it up altogether, saying it was fun while it lasted but life has more to offer than drug trips, particularly when the risks are so high.

We've seen what happened to Mrs. Brennan. Now let's take a look at another experience, this one by a woman two years the teacher's junior. It is not a pleasant story. Worse, while it began somewhat like Mrs. Brennan's, it ended in sheer tragedy. Contrary to Mrs. Brennan's reassurance that she found cannabis pleasant, relaxing, and "cool," the woman currently under discussion has dedicated the remaining years of her life to warning parents and youth about the dangers of this drug. "Society must say: do not touch it," she says, "leave it alone!"[7]

Last September, 1967, her son was a brilliant student. "Very bright, very able, with prospects of a fine career as a teacher," said his major professor in college. The young man held a master's degree in psychology and was studying for his doctorate in psychology under a federal grant. Then, one day, a friend introduced him to cannabis under the aegis of researching the drug and expanding the mind. Because the effects of the cannabis plant weren't as effective as mind-expanders as the young man had hoped, he soon turned to LSD. "Later," says his mother, "one of his kooky friends gave him STP and this caused his tailspin. This is the horrible part —a fellow student gave him STP knowing he had had a nervous breakdown." The breakdown had occurred after the youth had been on several cannabis trips. At this time, despite a happy marriage and a successful career, the young man began to question the validity of life. He became so depressed he attempted suicide. Failing this attempt, he voluntarily entered UCLA Hospital for psychiatric therapy.

The mother had frequently discussed her son's experiments with him, trying to persuade him to give them up. "We knew all about it," she said. "He told us all about it. We warned him, 'Son, if you smoke marijuana it will lead to something else,' but he pooh-poohed all our warnings." Instead, he insisted "They've been using it for thousands of years without harm. There's nothing to it. It's actually not as bad as alcohol."

Near the end of September the youth, obsessed by his drug-induced philosophies, entered the photo lab in Franz Hall at UCLA. He wrapped his head and face with gauze, put a plastic bag over the gauze and taped it around his neck. A scuba diver's mask was placed over his mouth. From it ran a hose that was connected to a nearby open gas jet. A roll of masking tape lay near the body. On it, written in blue ink, were the words, "I shall return." The following morning his professor found him dead of asphyxiation.

The mother lamented, "What they don't realize is that the effects are cumulative. If they don't get the results they think they should, they move on to something else."

In other words, social prominence or obscurity is not the important point. The important point is that potential users should know the whole range of evidence. It is not rational to consider only evidence that supports one's convictions. Look at it all and then decide.

Is there a safe use for cannabis?

"In my opinion," says Dr. Daniel Efron,[8] a psychopharmacologist with the National Institute of Mental Health, "at this moment we don't have enough scientific facts to anwer that question." "Medical scientists," agrees science writer Patricia McBroom, "don't know, for instance, whether marijuana poses a threat comparable to alcohol, or more serious, or less. They don't know whether chronic users undergo subtle personality changes, though there is a widespread impression that long-term users have an unusually depressed drive level. And they don't know how safe it is to smoke the weed occasionally, as a large group of Americans seems to be doing. The one thing they do know is that marijuana is not innocuous; but then neither is alcohol or tobacco."[9]

Considering the fact that at one time cannabis was employed for almost every known illness, this lack of certainty about its use may seem incongruous. But again we face the fact that current investigators are reticent to accept observations made by scientists in the past. Perhaps this is just as well, for as advances in investigation have shown, newer and more promising useful chemical activity has been found to be present in the active ingredients of cannabis. With the discovery in 1967 by scientists in both Israel and France of the exact synthesis of the natural tetrahydrocannabinols we can now reproduce the much-needed pure compounds for research.

These recent investigations have revealed that the THC's previously suspected and generally accepted as the active ingredients of cannabis are in effect two principal chemicals, delta[8] and delta[9] trans-tetrahydrocannabinol.[10] The chemical structure of these substances is highly unusual. They do not resemble that of other hallucinogens. Instead they occupy their own class. Studying cannabis with a newer, fresher viewpoint, various investigators have demonstrated activity ranging from antibacterial and anticonvulsive effects to anesthetic and analgesic properties. As this progress has been made, men such as Dr. Edward G. Taylor, who directs a research team at Princeton University, expresses the hope that cannabis may become the source of a whole new generation of drugs with a range of useful therapeutic functions.[11]

The fact that cannabis currently lacks the safety and effectiveness of newer drugs does not hinder adequate research but it does argue an air of caution among responsible scientists. At the moment the World Health Organization has stated that at present there is no justification for the medical use of cannabis. They make this recommendation because of the inadequacy of controls and dosage, and the lack of knowledge of the ultimate damage uncontrolled use of the drug could cause.[12] If, however, cannabis can be shown at a later date to possess valuable pharmacotherapeutic properties, and these properties can be isolated, there is no reason why they could not be included in the International Pharmacopoeia just as easily, if not more easily, than crude cannabis was excluded in the interest of public health.

The question is not whether cannabis should be investigated. The question is whether or not it is currently safe for use by non-scientists who want to play with the psychedelic effects of the drug. All current evidence points out that the use of crude cannabis is not only unsafe, it is fraught with considerable hazard to both society and the user.

It is true that with the amounts currently used by most American cannabis smokers, who rely on the home-grown variety and resist strengthening their cannabis with hashish or other more po-potent hallucinogens, most smokers experience euphoria and some sensory distortion and that is all. A few, however, will experience psychotic-like episodes at this level, and if the intake is increased five or six times over the euphoria-producing level, the cannabis trip begins to resemble the LSD experience.

Using pure delta[9] THC on forty human subjects, Dr. Harris Isbell of the University of Kentucky has been able to reproduce all the effects ever attributed to either mild or potent cannabis. He found the use of 18 milligrams of the chemical would almost without exception precipitate psychotic-like reactions in the user: hallucinations, depersonalization, loss of reality, distorted sight and hearing. If he dropped this dose to 2 or 3 milligrams he could reproduce the "usual" euphoric trip.[13]

If one used this lesser dose, Dr. Isbell says, the subjects were happy about the whole thing and referred to the cigarette as a "good reefer." "But if you keep turning the screws [increasing the dose]," Dr. Isbell notes, "all of a sudden they're on a trip watching their own burial." The fascinating thing about these men, the doctor further observed, is that they steadfastly refused to blame the adverse effects experienced with a higher chemical intake on the cannabis itself. "Occasionally, on the lower dose, a man would react peculiarly as though in a psychotic episode. But you wouldn't expect this in the majority of people," Dr. Isbell says.

As far as control is concerned in the light of his study (which tends to support the contention of the pro-cannabis people that "most users" do not experience adverse effects), Dr. Isbell says from his long and varied experience with drug users, "The local grass is probably pretty weak stuff but if you lower controls, watch out. You open the door to more potent stuff." It will be interesting to see how well our society listens to contemporary scientists who neither condemn nor condone the weed but who do, from experience in psychopharmacology, express concern that if we open the legal floodgates and create a true social menace by removing the current restraints on the use of cannabis by the scientifically uninitiated, we may find ourselves in the same intolerable position currently being experienced by other nations that made the same mistake.

Is cannabis addictive?

We've mentioned this question before—it is asked so frequently—and the use of the drug is excused so frequently on the basis of the argument that it is *not* addicting, that it is worth discussing this point again and amplifying it.

To begin with, the word *addiction* no longer means the same thing to everyone. Some people say they are addicted to eating or addicted to buying green shoes. This is nonsense. According to the World Health Organization three major effects must be present in order to achieve a true addiction: psychological dependence, tolerance, and physical dependence.[14]

Psychological dependence is a state of mind in which the user feels so deeply that he must have the drug in order to be content that he is driven almost obsessively to repeat his use. Tolerance is a pharmaco-physiological reaction in which the user's body becomes accustomed to a given amount of the drug and requires more of the drug on the next occasion in order to achieve the previous physical or psychological effects. Physical dependence is also a body reaction to the continued presence of the drug. Here, the user's body becomes so accustomed to the steady intake of the drug that it resents physically any removal of the drug. This resentment is manifested by withdrawal symptoms which may be mild in moderate users or quite severe in heavy users.

From the psychiatric point of view there is really little difference between cannabis dependence and narcotic addiction. When psychological factors cause the user to indulge in chronic compulsive abuse, the user is just as dependent or addicted as those we used to call simply addicts. The absence of physical dependence is relatively unimportant and constant reference to it merely confuses the issue. Physical dependence is quickly amenable to therapy. Once withdrawal is complete, the physical dependence is over with and presents no further problem. Not so the psychological dependence. This is the factor that causes drug abusers of every type to revert to the use of their drug choice time and time again whenever the going gets tough.

175

The WHO definition is adequate to explain scientifically the addiction problem. The issue, however, is confused by various "authorities" who like to seize upon the literal and ignore the implied aspects of medical statements. Fortunately, additional clarification of this point has been offered by men such as Maurer and Vogel who, in discussing physical dependence, state that the term

> must be used with qualifications, but of a different kind. There has been a notable tendency, especially on the part of the pharmacologists, to characterize addicting drugs as those which may not be used consistently over a long period of time without developing in the user a state of physical dependence.
>
> In the light of what is now known about addiction, this distinction is too narrow, or at least too narrow for the purposes of this study. Certainly it can now be shown that some of the drugs used compulsively and with very definite harm to the individual and to society are lacking in the power to produce true physical dependence in the user. Cocaine is a good example. Therefore, while physical dependence is one of the identifying characteristics of addicting drugs, it is not the sole one; nor do all addicting drugs produce physical dependence.[15]

Vogel, Isbell, and Chapman are more terse: "Drug addiction," they say, "may be defined as a state in which a person has lost the power of self-control with reference to a drug and abuses the drug to such an extent that the person or society is harmed."[16]

Where tolerance is the issue, it is generally agreed that, as far as *Cannabis americana* and *mexicana* are concerned, there is little need to increase the dose to obtain repetitive effect. Even this statement should be clarified. When one says this, he assumes that the users in this country will remain content with the milder forms of cannabis. Some may; but many will not. The constant increases in hashish confiscations by police indicate somebody no longer likes mild trips.

In this regard Dr. Dana Farnsworth notes that "The medical evidence is mounting that a good deal of marijuana currently sold to students is adulterated, indeed often 'laced' with mixtures of other hallucinogenic drugs to strengthen the effects. . . . The fact is, a person buying 'marijuana' has no way of knowing what he is actually getting."[17] This statement would not hold, of course, for those who buy their supply before the cannabis is manicured and rolled into joints. But a joint that has been prepared by someone else may contain drugs that are significantly more toxic than "mild" American cannabis. Supporting this idea, the American Medical Association's Committee on Alcoholism and Drug Dependence states, "When a teen-ager is handed a reefer, he can't be sure it's just marihuana. It may be hashish or a mixture containing hashish or even other more potent hallucinogens."[18]

No matter what anyone says, the debate as to whether cannabis is habit-forming or addicting will probably continue. Regardless of the variety of definitions and the claims of users that they can voluntarily discontinue use of the drug at any time without experiencing undue suffering or craving, Dr. David Ausubel of the Bureau of Educational Research of the University of Illinois says,

> their behavior indicates otherwise. When they anticipate separation from their source of supply, they take steps to accumulate sufficient reserve to "tide them over." Confirmed users bitterly resent deprivation and readily admit their future intentions to return to the drug as soon as conditions permit. According to one study, enforced deprivation results in "anxiety, restlessness, irritability or even a state of depression with suicidal phantasies, sometimes self-mutilating actions or actual suicidal attempts." These symptoms of psychological dependence are undoubtedly less pronounced and perhaps even absent in casual or recreational users.[19]

Ausubel speaks from the experience of long observation of a cross section of cannabis users as do the authorities he quotes. Unfortunately, while scientists such as Ausubel may reach the scholar, it is men like John Rosevear who catch the ears of the high school and college students. Such men issue observations based on limited exposure to the group of people most likely to develop psychological dependence on the drug. Marijuana contains a "mysterious safety valve," Rosevear insists. Then he parenthetically adds the qualifying statement that most youngsters seem to miss: *Depending on the personality of the user,* going beyond a euphoric state usually is difficult."[20] (Italics mine.)

Let's consider Ausubel's and Rosevear's statements a moment. Both men actually say the same thing, although one is conservative in opinion while the other is permissive. Ausubel stresses psychological dependence may occur to such a degree that it is difficult to distinguish the state from the older, poorly defined, state of "addiction." This concerns Ausubel because as a scientist he realizes the casual approach to this drug may be grossly detrimental to people who are susceptible to the effects of cannabis. Rosevear, on the other hand, who stresses the fun and relaxation aspects of the use of cannabis, dismisses the probability of detrimental effects with a wave of a parenthesis by saying "(depending on the personality of the user), going beyond a euphoric state usually is difficult." In effect, both men are saying this: some people may use it and enjoy it with no ill effects. But some others will become dependent on it.

Although most authorities will admit that cannabis can be habit-forming, the question of addiction has never really been solved. Is it just a matter of quarreling over words or have instances been noted in valid medical literature of true withdrawal from and physical dependence upon cannabis?

As a matter of fact, not all authorities agree with the statement that cannabis does not cause physical dependence or withdrawal. It is true that, with the milder forms of cannabis most often currently used in this country, physical dependence has not been reported. This is not true of *Cannabis indica.* In 1949 J. D. Fraser, the deputy medical superintendent at Whittingham Hospital, Lancashire, England, reported nine cases of acute withdrawal and physical dependence upon cannabis indica (actually to the THC in the plant).

"During the early days of a campaign in the Far East," he reported in the October 22, 1949, edition of *Lancet,*[21] "several cases of an acute psychosis associated with the withdrawal of *Cannabis indica* from addicts came to my notice. All those cases came in the first four weeks of the campaign and all were Indian troops.

"All these men had been indulging in ganja smoking for some years," Fraser noted, "and they soon began to notice signs of deprivation when they left India; two showed signs of extreme irritability on the sea voyage but they got over this when they managed to procure some more ganja from their comrades. On arrival at their destination all began to suffer from deprivation; the Indian hemp plant did not grow so widely, and ganja became difficult to obtain."

Each of these men, the author said, was a known ganja addict and each was regarded with a certain amount of fear and generally considered untrustworthy by his fellow soldiers. As time went on, irritability among the addicts increased. It culminated in sudden violence such as stabbing another man, striking out, or shooting at someone. Generally, the addict's military medical history went something like this: he was on guard duty when he suddenly began to fire away at the enemy; but no enemy was there. It was all a hallucination. This sort of conduct caused the man to be sent to the hospital for observation. The strange, often dangerous fact,

Fraser says, is that when the man arrived at the medical unit he usually appeared quiet and seemed apparently rational. He did appear depressed most of the time, but he ate well and appreciated attention. Many times unsuspecting medical officers would quickly return such a man to active duty thinking all was well only to find that after forty-eight to seventy-two hours there was an outburst of violence. This outburst was followed by an acute psychotic episode that lasted three to six weeks.

During the psychotic period the patient was excited, would shout and talk at great length, quarrel, and interfere with other patients. He would often strip himself naked, masturbate almost continuously and become totally unconcerned about his bowel and bladder habits. Some addicts would sing for hours at the top of their voices. If one of these men saw a nursing orderly or a medical officer, he would crawl abjectly along the floor and beg for some ganja. If he was given an ordinary cigarette he would chew it up or smoke it as quickly as possible. Most of these patients endured both visual and aural hallucinations, some of which were terrifying. They could understand what was being told them, but when they started to obey an order their attention would lag and they would start begging for some more ganja. After five to six weeks of this they again became quiet, cooperative, and well behaved, although all were weak and emaciated. As soon as possible the army returned them to India.

The author, in conclusion, remarks that it is clear that some *Cannabis indica* addicts cannot live without their drug if it is suddenly withdrawn. If they are deprived of it they develop a dangerous mental illness. While noting the total incidence of this type of reaction was probably small in the British Army, Fraser also felt that many cases occurred which did not come to the attention of medical officers. "Clearly it would be safer," he finished, "if known *Cannabis indica* addicts were not employed on foreign service." Unfortunately for Dr. Fraser, he made these observations without the assistance of those men who today insist that such things cannot happen because they have never seen them. Clearly it would have been much more palatable for Dr. Fraser if he could also have pretended that the situation never occurred and that the addicts he saw never existed. But they did.

Can cannabis hurt one physically?

Few really significant organic changes are demonstrable; there are, however, many less than desirable physical effects that accompany the use of cannabis. We quote Rosevear, not a man to overplay any undesirable effects of cannabis use:

When introduced into the system, marihuana affects two areas: the mind and the body. The effects come almost immediately (within a few minutes) when marihuana is smoked, and in a half hour to an hour when ingested. . . .

There are slight changes in the cardiovascular system; a small rise in blood pressure, an increase in heart beat, and some congestion around the eyes . . . but none of these changes are beyond the normal margin of safety. There is often a desire to urinate. The mouth and throat begin to feel dry, and thirst is realized. The appetite frequently grows enormous. Blood sugar and the basal metabolic rate are elevated, but here, too, not beyond the upper limits of normal. There is a pupil dilatation and the eyes' reflex to light is slow. The skin becomes sensitive to touch . . . certain feelings [occur] such as the top of the head flying off, the limbs becoming more mobile, and a general strength or lightness sometimes appears, indicating a stimulating effect. . . . The area surrounding the eyes often gets reddish, and the throat feels dry. The flow of saliva seems slowed down, for the smoker often desires any liquid or sweet. The almost irrational desire to put some object into the mouth to quell this feeling is referred to as a "regression to the oral stage." Perception of distance is not impaired by sight, but physical actions, such as walking up a flight of stairs, often seems like an entire journey.[22]

Torald Sollman, in his *Manual of Pharmacology*, supports Rosevear's observations, amplifying the description with the information that it takes about two grains of the solid extract whether oral or smoked, to produce the effect. He, too, points out that the chronic user suffers from the digestive phenomenon, anorexia (loss of appetite), and dryness or burning thirst, stating categorically a fact we all realize, namely that "the phenomena differ in kind as well as in degree according to the individual personality and dispositions, the surrounding and the mental preparation."[23]

"Toxic doses," Sollman says, "cause vertigo [dizziness] and collapse with soft arrhythmic [irregular] pulse and blood concentrations sometimes to 50 percent. Serious poisoning is rare, since the margin between the effective and fatal dose is wide; the intravenous fatal dose for dogs is a hundred times the narcotic dose." Obviously, then, cannabis is about as safe a hallucinogen as one can use assuming one doesn't mind taking psychotoxic drugs.

Incidentally, it is often said by pro-cannabis speakers that no death has ever been reported from the use of cannabis. This is not true. Walton refers to deaths directly related to the use of cannabis, but the number is so small as to be insignificant. Nevertheless, it is a misrepresentation of the facts to assert that *no* deaths have ever occurred from the drug.[24]

Americans, with their low potency cannabis, lack adequate experience by which to properly judge the effects of the drug. Furthermore, law enforcement has hampered importation of stronger varieties, particularly after FBN Commissioner Harry J. Anslinger notably called this country's attention to the dangers of the drug. Thus, America lacks the documentation accumulated by India where, according to Dr. David Ausubel, "Chronic addiction is more common and of longer standing, reliable evidence of damaged health has been reported for 42 percent of chronic users. Among the more typical symptoms are: congestion of the eyes, pharyngitis, laryngitis, chronic bronchitis, loss of weight, diarrhea alternating with constipation and depression of sexual activity."[25]

The interesting matter of cannabis and sexuality will be discussed later, but in treating here of possible physical harm from cannabis, it should be noted that Dr. David Smith, of Haight-Ashbury, recently testified that sexual depression from the use of drugs was one problem that caused users in the Haight-Ashbury district to come to doctors for help. Smith also noted that this effect has occurred with the abuse of amphetamines which, while they facilitate the sex *drive,* may cause males to experience difficulty in *performance.*[26]

The Chopras, writing of the physical effects of chronic cannabis abuse in India, state: "Excessive dosage of these drugs repeated daily upsets in the alimentary and excretory systems. Appetite declines and the food is not properly assimilated. The addict may lose weight rapidly and may suffer from general cachexia [wasting away]; the skin becomes pale and dry and is often covered with scales; the nails and the teeth decay and the hair, which is frequently affected, becomes dry and loses its lustre."[27] The best way to summarize the matter is to state that bad effects from the use of cannabis exist but usually occur with chronic abuse of high-potency cannabis.

There is little question but that an acute and chronic toxicity resulting from the use of cannabis exists, Dr. David Smith[28] said recently, but this syndrome is so buried in misinformation that users lose interest in discussing it. The problem goes even deeper than that. Evidence of chronic physical change has been accumulated over the centuries, but each civilization, because it reacts differently to varying potencies of the drugs, acquires a new set of observations and interpretations. In America, we would be better off, assuming that we can keep stronger cannabis and contaminated cannabis from becoming a major issue, to realize that the extreme effects such as have been found in India are not currently in evidence; and thus we should cease trying to overimpress the public with data that cannot be correlated with current observations.

Does cannabis cause sexual excitation and increased sexual powers? Is it an aphrodisiac?

"It is true that some individuals experience a marked stimulation of [sexual] desires," Walton says, "but in a great proportion of other instances, no such impulses are evident. The effect, again, is very probably due to removal of the usual restraints and correspondingly to the release of the more primitive impulses."[29] Vogel[30] notes that some people actually take the drug in the hope that it will preserve, improve, or maintain their sexual powers. Since strong expectations may exist in that direction and since cannabis creates receptivity to suggestions, use of the drug may actually influence sexual performance. This, however, is temporary at best.

The ability of cannabis to enhance sexuality lies in its peculiar alterations of time-space relationships and its propensity to increase the acuity of the senses. Additionally, by removing normal restraints and releasing inhibitions and by making the individual more susceptible to suggestion, cannabis use makes participation in sexual activity not only pleasant, if this happens to be what the user has in mind, but the obvious thing to do. Ausubel notes:

"The apparent erotic stimulation induced by marijuana in certain individuals, therefore, corresponds essentially to the release of inhibited personality trends. These persons prior to drug use tend to be excessively preoccupied with sexual gratification. Many also exhibit infantile and homosexual tendencies. In addition, the drug increases self-confidence and eliminates apprehension about the receptivity of the contemplated sex partner. Many [users] report that the sensual aspects of sexual enjoyment are prolonged as a consequence of the exaggerated perception of elapsed time. Exhibitions of perverted sexual practices ("circuses") are not an uncommon feature at "tea parties."[31]

Arguing against the concept that cannabis can enhance sexuality, some people note that Eastern monks and fakirs have used hemp from earliest times to turn off their sexual desires and heighten their visual and auditory contemplations of eternity. Of course they have; some still do. This is the remarkable thing about cannabis. Whatever you were before you took the drug, whatever you had in mind as the goal to reach while on it, is increased and enhanced by the use of the drug. If one wishes to pray, one may think he is in intimate contact with the Eternal; if one wishes to copulate, he can pretend he is a satyr or she a nymph. Cannabis enables one to regress to an earlier stage of life when the very innocence of being young and uninhibited makes it possible to do things that the adult ego-censorship would prohibit. Whether or not this is a good thing is open to debate.

It is well to reflect that most of the cannabis users in this country are youths between the ages of fourteen and twenty-five. This age span needs no aphrodisiac to stimulate either interest or capacity to perform. If young men have the sex act in mind when they use the drug they will probably move toward a selected partner. The woman, for her part, will find it easier to acquiesce. As for homosexuals, a growing number have found this drug an ideal releaser of restraints and use it to sidetrack the usual inhibitions, suspicions, and guilt associated with socially unapproved sexuality.

The interesting thing is that actual sexual congress by young people while on marijuana is very largely a projection on the part of adults. In the majority of instances the outcome seems to be more the fulfillment of a whimsical quip by Shaw, who noted that most sex occurs because people are bored and have nothing better to do. Contemporary cannabis users have a lot to do while on cannabis and sex is only one of a long list. As for those who "wouldn't touch a girl while up on pot," well, let's face it: they probably wouldn't have touched her while off pot either.

How does cannabis affect the mind?

Terribly. But again it depends on all the variables that crop up when one discusses cannabis. The most critical variable in this instance is the emotional stability of the user. Even then a true knowledge of his stability may not be gained until he goes off the deep end because of his use of a psychotoxin.

Recently Dr. Dana L. Farnsworth, Director of the Harvard University Health Services, issued a warning to his students which read in part: "Marijuana has a chemical effect on ordinary consciousness; ideas are rapid, disconnected, and uncontrollable. There may be feelings of well-being, exaltation, and excitement—that is, being 'high.' Or, at other times there may be a 'down' with moodiness, fear of death, and panic . . . large doses may produce confusion, disorientation, and increased anxiety. In a few instances marijuana has produced psychoses, as does LSD."[32]

California Assemblyman William Campbell[33] recently listed a few of the detrimental effects cannabis causes to the mind, basing his observations on reports by accepted (at least by government and medicine) authorities who have noted these effects from their experience:

> First, cannabis distorts time and space relationships so that one finds it difficult, if not impossible, to relate to reality.
>
> Second, it decreases inhibitions making it easier to express anti-social tendencies previously held in control by religious or social inhibitions.
>
> Third, it alters perception making visual, auditory, gustatory, olfactory and touch sensitivity much more acute. In doing so, it makes it that much harder for the user to detect the real experience from the imagined or from that which is toxically produced by chemicals.
>
> Fourth, as the dose of THC increases, one's sense of interpretation is altered both as to one's own ability and limitions and as to relationship with other people and things.
>
> Fifth, in high dosage it produces hallucinations which may be either pleasant or unpleasant.
>
> Sixth, it can produce toxic psychoses which can alter the life of the individual, not only during but long after the drug abuse episode. Cases of gross panic and fear, depersonalization, gross confusion and disorientation, acute depression, paranoid phenomena and schizophrenic behavior have been reported.
>
> Seventh, cannabis use can produce flashback phenomena if the proper association is present. These flashbacks are recurrences of the marijuana experience and occur when the individual may be unable either to control or emotionally encompass the accompanying sensory distortion. Cannabis possesses, in the flashback experience, the Pavlovian set of circumstances referred to as the conditioned response.
>
> Eighth, the use of cannabis can recapitulate the hallucinogenic experience elicited by a previous drug experience with LSD. (This is also true of other psychotoxins, including alcohol).

Concerning the predictability of the mental and emotional response to the use of cannabis, Dr. Robert S. De Ropp, a physician not known for his antipathy to cannabis, says, "We cannot tell in what form it (cannabis, or more properly THC) enters the body. We cannot tell in what form it enters the brain or in what manner it affects the chemistry of the brain cells. Despite the tremendous recent interest in psychochemistry this important group of compounds has been ignored and we know as little about the mode of action of the hemp drug on the brain as did Hasan-Ibn-Sabbah when he fed it to his followers a thousand years ago."[34]

But this we do know: cannabis may confuse the mind, impair judgment, distort perception, increase suggestibility, weaken will power, and diminish the faculty of self-criticism to the extent that many times the user may arrive at the inaccurate conclusion that he belongs to a superior order of beings. Just as it may relax anxieties for most casual users, cannabis can erode ambition. It can encourage irresponsibility, and remove the individual from the mainstream of life by diminishing or diverting into negative channels creativity which could benefit all society; this is wasted because the user is too busy turning on and ultimately dropping out.

Fortunately, and yet unfortunately because of its ultimate effect, the foregoing assessment applies to only a minority of American cannabis users as of this moment. Enough users are involved, however, so that the situation is serious. There is a real danger for the user in becoming dependent upon cannabis. When users repeatedly get high they reach a point where they don't want to come down. In fact they don't want to do anything but take cannabis. They find a world where they think they have no problems and they become social dropouts. Many of these young users dream dreams of accomplishment, but when they come down they find their experience was a dream, a bubble, and that things are worse than ever. Such persons are so depressed by this revelation that they rush back to the drug again to escape the cold fact that they aren't as capable as the drug made them feel they were.

Dr. David Smith, in relating his experiences at the Haight-Ashbury clinic,[35] notes frequently that he has seen no organic problems, significant hallucinations, or psychotic episodes in cannabis users in his area. Since most of these users move on to other medications, some of which are tremendously psychotoxic, it is not surprising that the effects of a mild drug seem pale in comparison. But in the Haight those who use cannabis also tend to use other drugs. "Speed freaks" (methamphetamine users), for instance, tend to use cannabis thirty times more often than nonamphetamine users.

Smith has seen, however, and seems disturbed by, a problem he refers to as the amotivational syndrome. In this syndrome a general apathy occurs to the cannabis user, a fragmentation of his personality structure which causes him to become unmotivated and disinterested in any purposeful activity. Ultimately, unless this process is interrupted, the user turns into a social misfit.

During his recent visit to America Dr. Constandinos J. Miras of the University of Athens, Greece, commented on this amotivational syndrome, sparking the press to one of its most enthusiastic anti-cannabis responses in some time. "I can recognize a chronic marijuana user from afar," Dr. Miras was quoted as saying, "by the way he walks, talks and acts. You begin to see the personality changes that typify the longtime user—the slowed speech, the lethargy, the lowered inhibitions and the loss of morality. They will accept as perfectly plausible things which five years ago they did not even like to hear discussed. They will become suddenly violent. They will even kill."[36]

Dr. Miras mentioned work being done which points strongly toward permanent organic changes in brain structure as a result of cannabis use. Noting that this work was experimental and based on *Cannabis indica* effects, he stressed that the main danger for youth lies in their losing interest and ambition and drive. "What will be the future of a nation whose people have no interest in success?" he asked. In observing and following a number of chronic cannabis users in the Los Angeles area over a five to six year period, this author has found Dr. Miras' observations all too accurate.

How harmful is cannabis to one's mind? Well, the La Guardia Report (which is not, as some claim, especially pro-cannabis, if one reads the fine print) states, "The conclusion seems warranted that given the potential makeup and the right time and environment, Marijuana may bring on a true psychotic state."[37] But psychosis is not at the moment one of our pressing problems in America. Apathy and drug-induced loss of motivation is the real issue. Psychic dependence is serious, says Dr. David Smith.[38] Users have to accept that there is such a thing as a chronic-abuse syndrome, and that such a syndrome can impair their growth. They have to realize that some users may take years to amotivate and not show it readily because it takes so long. But others may amotivate in a short time.

The variability of cannabis action on each person rests heavily on his stability. The total effect of the drug upon the mind, therefore, is unpredictable and is potentially dangerous. "The drug can cause deep anxiety and panic,"[39] *Newsweek* wrote in a special report, "again depending on the user's personality. A high dose may produce vivid hallucinations similar to an LSD trip. Even normal doses of marijuana can bring out underlying psychotic symptoms or psychological instabilities: feelings of paranoia may be increased under pot."

In spite of these warnings some youngsters prefer to believe the only way to find the truth is to experiment personally. Many labor under the delusion that pot can stimulate creative drive and profound thought. In rebuttal to this notion New York Columbia University psychiatric consultant Dr. Robert S. Liebert says, "When I talk to a kid who is 'turned on' I have the sense of relating through a glass partition."[40] Where motivation is concerned, notes Dr. Sanford Feinglass of the University of California Medical School, "Even if marijuana does release inhibitions it is not certain that the user will be moved to act."[41] "That's the thing I really don't understand about pot," a young user told this author. "When I smoke it I think about doing great things but somehow as long as I smoke it I never get around to doing them."

Despite the observations of other nations and the outlawing of cannabis by every major and most minor nations of the world, Americans still have to try pot out for themselves, it seems, and be shown irrevocable proof that cannabis can cause harm. Oddly, being American, they will throw out a whole crop of cranberries at Thanksgiving because there was some question that they had been contaminated by insecticides; yet they will endanger their lives and civil liberties to use a drug that other nations have discarded as useless and dangerous.

Cannabis opens the mind and enhances creativity. Right?

Sadly, no. This we can prove. But let us begin with a story. Once upon a time some six centuries ago there lived a man by the name of Nasreddin Hodja whose feats were so remarkable that he became a legend in the Middle East. Hodja was, among other things, very curious about hashish. He had heard all the fourteenth century talk about how much fun it was, and how it wouldn't hurt him; so one day he bought a stash, smoked it, and wandered off to the Turkish bath to enjoy the effects in a swirl of steam. After a while, Hodja became a bit irritated. He experienced absolutely nothing. Convinced he had been cheated he rushed out on the street, headed for the druggist's. Midway a friend stopped him and asked what was going on. "I thought smoking hashish would do something to me," Hodja replied, "but as you can see I'm still what I was. I'm going to get the real stuff from the apothecary. I have a feeling he's cheated me." The friend smiled and nodded his head, then gave Hodja some advice. "Before you go all the way, Hodja, old friend," said the man, "go back to the bath and put on your clothes."[42]

Henri Michaux puts it a little more scientifically. "Don't forget," he warns his readers (he was speaking of mescaline, but his observations apply with equal force to cannabis), "that you have swallowed poison. Psychological explanations are all too tempting. Tracing everything to psychology is poor psychology." Michaux continues:

> The modulations, indeed, which "hemp" is able to achieve from such neutral beginnings are so astounding, so wondrous, so demonstrative of its superhuman power, so luminous, that no metaphysical brain, even with the most magnificent idea, could equal them. . . . There is no greater miracle of the "grasping intellect." Thus it is not surprising that these prodigious "exchanges" have given many a drug addict, even among the most mediocre, a somewhat exalted idea of his intelligence. No one, in fact, has a greater density of ideas than they do at certain moments, nor is capable of more unexpected association of ideas—of which they subsequently have not the slightest recollection.[43]

Where music is concerned the myth exists that jazz musicians play much better when on cannabis. It is true they are less inhibited and probably tire less easily, but there it stops. The habit is so common among musicians, Walton writes, "that it may properly be considered a special occupational hazard. . . . There is very little probability that an individual's performance is in any degree improved over that of his best capabilities. As judged by objectively critical means, the standards of performance are no doubt lowered."[44]

In 1934 Gerard Piel wrote an article for a national magazine about the use of cannabis by musicians and included the blatantly false assertion that while on cannabis the "swing musician ascends to new peaks of virtuosity."[45] This interested Dr. C. Knight Aldrich, an assistant surgeon for the United States Public Health Service, who gave cannabis (synthetic THC) to twelve musicians prior to their playing and administered a group of tests that experts refer to as "outstandingly the most important battery of tests in the field of music," Aldrich suspected that the release of inhibitions by cannabis use might bring out latent talents or evoke a more intense emotional performance. Yet he also recognized that one could not trust the using subject's evaluation of his own performance. So he ran his own careful tests. Here is his conclusion: "No improvement was observed in the musical capability, as tested by the Seashore measures of musical talents, of twelve former users of marijuana after ingestion of satisfying amounts of parahexyl compound, a synthetic marihuana-like substance. Although 9 out of the 12 subjects achieved poorer scores after using the drug than on the previous trial, 8 out of 12 expressed the opinion that their scores had improved, and none recognized a loss of efficiency."[46]

"The very common idea of improved performance is based on several features which can give considerable apparent support to such an impression," Walton notes.[47] "There is an increased sensitivity to sound and a keener appreciation of rhythm and timing. These phenomena, as judged by objective criteria, probably do not exist except during certain early phases of the drug's effects. The release of inhibitions may uncover latent talents which previously had been subject to personality restraints. The wild, emotional character of performance can be intensified and for certain audiences this may represent improvement although it would not be so acknowledged by an individual of cultivated musical appreciation.

In addition, we even have the testimony of author William Burroughs that "unquestionably this drug is very useful to the artist, activating trains of association that would otherwise be inaccessible, and I owe many of the scenes in *Naked Lunch* directly to the use of cannabis."[48] The irony is that Burroughs meant his remark as an endorsement.

American cannabis is so weak and lasts for such a short time that none of the effects described by hashish ever occur. Why do some people keep attacking marijuana when it is not the same as hashish and, in fact, comes from an entirely different plant?

The truth about marijuana, hashish, and any number of synonyms for this plant, or its product, is that it all comes from the same source. There is only one marijauna, or hashish, plant. It is *Cannabis sativa*. One genus, one species. All the rest of the subdivisions are *varieties* of the mother plant. They differ in potency for reasons previously described. Essentially this is due to varied geographical locations and climatic conditions.

American marijuana is a cousin to hashish, the latter being some five to six times more potent because the cannabinol content of the resin of *Cannabis indica* is more toxic than that found in the resin of *Cannabis americana* or *mexicana*. If cannabis use in the United States were static, there might be less cause for alarm than there is, but Americans do not seem content to continue to use poor-quality cannabis. A growing number of users keep on the lookout for increasingly powerful types of "good grass." Because of this, "Acapulco gold" or "Panama red" have become very popular. For the same reasons, the hashish market is steadily expanding in America. Users no longer just buy "pot"; they are becoming selective. This may not be true for the unsophisticated user who is curious to try once and probably not return to the drug again, but it is true for a significant segment of the experienced repeating users.

Today's buyer can obtain almost any effect he wants wrapped into the prepared "joint." If he wants to nod he gets marijuana soaked in opium. The one who wants a psychological trip, on the other hand, dips his reefer in LSD, STP, or any of the readily available hallucinogens that provide bizarre mental experiences.

One does not have to resort to these esoteric compounds, however, if he really wants to hallucinate and "mindblow." He can start with "mild" American or Mexican cannabis and if he persists he can obtain the same effect acquired from any of the stronger hallucinogens. How much he will need to do this is unpredictable because of all the variables. Some users can obtain the effect with just a few cigarettes; others have to take pipefuls in order to reach the same high. But this much we know: cannabis is capable of producing all the weird emotional and mental effects that can be obtained with other hallucinogenic substances including those experienced from the use of LSD. The difference between the mild form of American cannabis and the more potent forms of hallucinogens is primarily one of use pattern and amount of drug. It is true most American users at the current moment are staying on the conservative side of cannabis use. But if experiences in other countries provide any lesson or indication, we can expect that a segment of American users will do everything they can to increase the potency of their drugs until the products preferred will resemble those found in countries where resin with high cannabinol content is readily available.

Is there a "typical" cannabis user and can he be expected to behave in a given manner if he is dependent upon the drug?

Once there might have been a single typical cannabis user. No more. Elsewhere in this book we have tried to categorize loosely today's users, but it is recognized that even a loose categorization is inadequate. Perhaps we should here refer to Dr. David Ausubel's[49] classification. Ausubel uses the etiological headings used by some authorities for opium addicts and applies them to cannabis users. These are: primary users, symptomatic users, and reactive users. In addition there are some subdivisions that are found in all three categories: recreational users, who use it simply for fun, habitual users, who are usually inadequate personalities, and two less frequently encountered groups—those who use the drug to augment their appreciation of artistic and creative activity and an even smaller group of those who use it to help them in the performance of premeditated criminal activity.

The primary users, Ausubel says, are those who need the drug to help them adjust. These are inadequate personalities, anxious, neurotic people, and those who are depressed. The symptomatic users are antisocial people who use the drug to aid their already antisocial activities. The reactive users are preponderantly normal, usually teenage, youths who use it as a status symbol or to keep up with the rest of the group.

The interesting thing about Ausubel's discussion is that he emphasizes, as do most students of cannabis abuse, the importance of understanding the inadequate personality, because it is this group that constitutes the major social problem where the legalization of cannabis is concerned. The hazard in this instance is that the inadequate personality is drawn to the use of drugs and, being marginally adjusted, he will often fall into overt antisocial behavior, although previously he was in reasonable, if not total, control.

Ausubel believes that the inadequately adjusted group constitutes the habitual user segment of cannabis society. He calls them immature, emotionally unstable people who are unable to face reality or endure any stress or deprivation. They have a low frustration threshold and they cannot stand to be disciplined. Whenever they face conflict they attempt to resort to hedonistic behavior which pacifies them much as a bottle or nipple will pacify an anxious infant. If they cannot obtain adequate pacification, or if the drug they choose makes it easier for them to be aggressive, they can become socially disruptive.

Hedonism is the concept that best describes this group of inadequate personality drug users. It may be defined as the philosophy that pleasure and/or happiness is the sole or chief good in life. It is reiterated in the drug user jargon of the day that says, "What's the harm in doing your own thing if you don't hurt anybody?" Characteristically, the hedonistic cannabis user comes from a broken home, a poverty stricken home, or one in which there is continual domestic crisis. Most often all three elements are present.

One commonly finds in such a home a mother with a high and exacting moral standard of behavior and a father who is morally lax. Early in life the child reacts to this by having frequent nightmares, enuresis, and other symptoms that indicate he is operating under severe emotional stress. More important, he shows by reacting this way that he is not communicating well or interrelating well with his parents, usually his father but often his mother as well.

As he grows older he shows other signs of emotional immaturity. His school attendance becomes irregular. His grades are poor. Usually his mental ability is much higher than his scholastic achievement. As a youngster he is often involved in sexual misadventures, gambling, and theft. Frequently he is in conflict with authoritarian figures such as police and teachers. Once he leaves school, either by dropping out or barely squeezing through, he follows the same irregular pattern of behavior in job employment and credit instability. He develops a nomadic tendency. Quite often his only aggressive outlet for his hostility and anxiety is through sexual encounters of one sort or another.

If he manages to get into the service the situation is no better. According to Ausubel, the inadequate personality does quite poorly in the service. He shirks duty, is insubordinate, and is frequently hauled before disciplinary boards and/or courts martial. For this sort of person cannabis seems to have an "adjustive value"; it pulls him into line in his own (but not necessarily others') thinking because it gives him a sense of well-being and helps him "cope with reality." It gives him unwarranted feelings of self-confidence and releases aggressive and erotic tendencies. It also reduces the anxiety he would normally feel when participating in socially unacceptable hedonistic gratifications. In other words, it makes him more of what he was before he took the drug. The problem is that what he was was hardly acceptable then and now that he is more of what he was, the situation becomes intolerable for people around him.

The inadequate personality who uses marijuana habitually, Ausubel says, resembles his opiate-addicted counterpart. There are, however, some striking differences. Most cannabis addicts come from homes that have greater emotional conflict and exhibit a greater difference between the moral standards of the father and mother. The child usually reacts to this by becoming aggressive and/or sexually hedonistic. He may, on the other hand, however, just drop out.

When cannabis comes along it is suitable for either purpose. He can "turn on" sexually or he can turn it all off and become asexual and introverted. The heroin addict has no such alternative. If he becomes hooked on opiates he can only turn off and nod out, becoming aggressive only when he is in need of his drug to relieve both physical and psychological withdrawal pain. The cannabis user can swing either way depending on his intent and goal.

In a technical résumé Ausubel says this of the cannabis versus the heroin user: "The inadequate personality who turns to the opiates . . . must be primarily concerned with attaining the nonspecific psychological aspects of euphoria—the aspects that are realized by inhibition of the self-critical faculty and by elimination of primary drives. The marijuana user, on the other hand, is more actively concerned with experiencing the sensuous and hedonistic components of drug-induced euphoria."

How can you say cannabis is bad when one of the top officials in Washington, Dr. Goddard, said he'd rather have his daughter smoke cannabis than take a drink of liquor.

Did he indeed? What actually happened to Dr. Goddard was that he was misquoted. It happens to all public speakers now and then. This author remembers having given a talk on cannabis at which the question was asked, "If a person smoked two joints a day or two packages of cigarettes a day which would be more physically harmful to the smoker?" The answer, obviously, was the two packages of cigarettes would cause more physical harm. The following day a reporter blithely wrote the following: "When asked about tobacco and marijuana, Dr. Bloomquist said that tobacco was more harmful than pot." Having had this experience I find it easy to understand what happened to Federal Food and Drug Commissioner Dr. James L. Goddard.

Dr. Goddard was holding an informal press conference following a talk at the University of Minnesota when a question about cannabis was asked. A campus correspondent, probably indulging in wishful thinking, rushed what he thought was the answer to the question to UPI which released it on October 17, 1967, stating that Dr. Goddard had affirmed he would not object to his daughter's smoking marijuana any more than if she drank a cocktail. The *New York Times* front paged the story and the *Washington Post* headlined, "FDA HEAD DOUBTS POT IS WORSE THAN ALCOHOL." The newspapers were reporting honestly what their correspondent had told them.

In Washington during the next three weeks some angry congressmen demanded Goddard resign. Medical authorities across the nation besieged Dr. Goddard's office with calls accusing him of doing "irreparable damage across the college campuses as well as in the high schools." But as the noise began to hit its peak it was discovered that a local radio station had recorded Dr. Goddard's actual remarks and that a transcript of the comments was available. Referring to it, Dr. Goddard remarked dryly, "You will note that I did not advocate free use of marijuana, did not dismiss its possible dangers to health, nor did I fail to recognize the fact that possession of marijuana is illegal."[50]

As for the comment Goddard was supposed to have made about objections to his daughter's smoking marijuana, the FDA head had actually replied: "We've discussed this at home. I would [object] in terms of the law today and any possible long-term effect." Later in amplifying this statement Dr. Goddard said, "I wouldn't want my daughter or any other young woman to use marijuana until we know more about it." Shortly thereafter, UPI, which had been as misled as everyone else, sent Goddard a letter of apology:[51] "UPI erred in attributing to you an unqualified statement which in fact was considerably qualified." But the damage was done for many who read the first report and now would never believe that the retraction was anything more than another government plot spurred on by the cannabis-hating establishment to keep the real truth hidden.

Regarding Dr. Goddard's comments concerning cannabis and alcohol, this is the exact exchange from the radio station broadcast transcript:

> Question: Would you describe it [cannabis] as being more dangerous than alcohol? Marijuana is more serious than alcohol?
>
> Goddard: Well, trying to compare two different drugs is a very risky business itself. They have quite different mechanisms of action; alcohol's a depressant, where marijuana's a mild hallucinogen, at best, or maybe a euphoric.
>
> Now they both share some properties in common, however, they both distort our sense of reality, and therefore it's dangerous to operate heavy equipment or drive a vehicle when we're under the influence of either one of these.
>
> Alcohol, probably lends itself more readily to control on the part of the individual, with respect to the dosage he's receiving than marijuana does, at least to the inexperienced.
>
> So, there are some similarities, but there are also some differences. And as I've mentioned many times, we don't know what the long term effects of smoking marijuana or

using marijuana in other forms might be, and we have to carry out this kind of research before, I for one, would be satisfied to say that the drug is safe under any conditions.[52]

Later, before a House Commerce Committee meeting in which Goddard was asked to explain his erroneously reported statement, the FDA chief made himself quite clear: "I did not, and I do not, condone the use of marijuana. I did not, and I do not, advocate the abolition of controls over marijuana. I did not, and I do not, propose 'legalizing' the drug." While admitting that he does have reservations about current penalties imposed on cannabis users which he feels "prevent full and effective protection of the public interest in the matter of abused drugs of any kind," he stressed that much is unknown about marijuana and its effects.[53]

"No one in the scientific or medical communities is satisfied with the level of knowledge we have," he said. "Clearly, while the answers to these questions are being formulated by the scientific community our enforcement efforts in the Food and Drug Administration as well as in the Bureau of Narcotics must continue." The FDA head also reported that marijuana use has been present in nine out of ten investigations of LSD and other hallucinogens of that type. Commenting on the experience of FDA agents and observations made on the effects of using cannabis, Goddard said, "The most common reaction to the use of marijuana is development of a state of mind in which ideas seem disconnected, uncontrolled, and freely flowing. Perception is disturbed, minutes seem to be hours and seconds may be broadened and objects may appear far away." And finally he noted, "With large doses vivid hallucinations may occur and panic with a fear of death may make the experience highly unpleasant."

Now that's telling it like it is.

Name one, just one, social activity where the use of cannabis can really be proved to cause a problem.

Just one? Let's talk about driving a car. A number of very interesting people have discussed the cannabis-car accident problem. Timothy Leary, for instance, was recently discoursing along with Richard Alpert on the subject of consciousness expansion. "The danger, of course," Leary said.

> is not physical. A recent editorial in the *Medical Tribune* clearly recognizes the physiological safety of consciousness-expanding drugs. Nor is the danger psychological. In studies reported by Ditman, McGlothlin, Leary, Savage, up to 90 per cent of subjects taking these drugs in supportive environ-

ments testify enthusiastically. The danger is not physical or psychological but social-political, for the effect of consciousness-expanding drugs will be to transform our concepts of human nature, of human potentialities, of existence. . . . The political issue involves control: "automobile" means that the free citizen moves *his* own car in external space. Internal automobile. Auto-administration. The freedom and control of one's experiential machinery. Licensing will be necessary. You must be trained to operate. You must demonstrate your proficiency to handle consciousness-expanding drugs without danger to yourself or the public. The Fifth Freedom—the freedom to expand your own consciousness—cannot be denied without due cause.[54]

Now, the automobile is recognized as being a dangerous, complicated piece of machinery. It is further recognized that people who are up on drugs, any drugs, which distort the mind are far from capable of operating a vehicle. License or no license, training or no training, freedom or no freedom, a man who cannot operate his thinking processes cannot be trusted to operate a complicated vehicle. This is particularly true when the vehicle operation may endanger the rights and lives of others. Since it is so, how safe is it for the same type of people to expand their consciousness without danger to themselves or the public?

Let's take a look at the comments of another pro-cannabis leader and see what he has to say in this respect. Rosevear, in this context, is discussing crime and pointing out that people become so relaxed and happy on cannabis that, according to his observations, "it is difficult to see how the intoxicated could motivate himself adequately to go through the motions of any crime."

"Many who are under the drug's spell," he says, "find that simple acts, such as getting a glass of water, are laborious. . . . It is difficult, if not impossible, to imagine how this type of intoxication could allow a person to write a bad check. And to suggest that this kind of intoxication could allow anyone to fulfill the complications of a murder is absurd."[55]

Interesting, these observations by Rosevear. May we ask: Do cannabis users drive when they are using the drug?

"In areas where police are especially diligent about arresting marijuana smokers," Rosevear says (although not in direct reply to the question stated above), "the 'pot parties' become infrequent, and the practice of clandestine smoking is considered fairly dangerous. When that happens, the occasion of smoking takes on other qualities. For instance, smoking in an automobile is considered especially safe, for if the police stop the car, the possessors merely sprinkle their pot to the wind. The driver of the car smokes if he feels he can 'handle' the situation—if his judgment will not be seriously impaired."[56]

Elsewhere Rosevear asks: "Will it be transported in cars? Will it be smoked in cars? One might be justifiably alarmed if he saw an obviously intoxicated group of people climb into an auto and head for the expressway. Whether the intoxication was due to pot, whiskey or pills makes little difference. What can be done about preventing people from driving an auto under pot's influence? The answer is maddeningly clear: absolutely nothing. Just like alcohol. Further, if a person is high and chooses to drive, and is stopped by the police, he can deny knowledge of marijuana and there is no way to prove otherwise.

"Some people say that if they're high and have to drive, they must concentrate hard on the driving, and all the fun part of the high is used up. Others," Rosevear continues, "who have smoked pot for a long time, drive as carefully high as not. Further, if the drug's use is as widespread as opinions often indicate, then the lack of auto accidents attributable to it might point out that the smokers are using unusually sound judgment."

"However," Rosevear continues, "unlike alcohol drinkers, most pot smokers studiously avoid driving while high. Nevertheless, he who is compelled to try and transcend his reality by some other spirit than alcohol is certainly not 'one of the boys.' A primitive, subtle taboo acts as a definite segregator."[57]

The matter of driving while on cannabis is getting to be an international problem. According to Drs. Dana Farnsworth and Curtis Pound of the Harvard University of Health Service, "A dangerous effect from marijuana is the slowing of reflexes. Since marijuana also causes distortion of reality, particularly of the sense of time, the drug is frequently a cause of automobile accidents."[58] There's more to it than that. Check the remarks previously made concerning the effects of even mild cannabis use on the eyes, the reference to the flashback phenomena, and the production of visual and auditory hallucinations, and the picture begins to take form.

The fallacies of Rosevear's arguments are clear: on the one hand he acknowledges that marijuana incapacitates the user for many normal and simple activities; on the other he ignores the obvious dangers of driving while under the influence of the drug. The testimony of the doctors of the Harvard Health Service suggests, moreover, that there is a record of cannabis-associated automobile accidents. And there is other testimony of the same kind.

In Mexico, says Dr. Pablo Wolff, and in Cuba, "numerous traffic accidents . . . are attributed to the use made of the herb by some drivers, especially of buses! This is possible due to its influence on the perception both of time and space, which prevents the correct localization of objects."[59] In France, according to a statement made by the French delegation before the United Nations Commission on Narcotic Drugs in 1963,[60] concern was expressed over the high rate of road accidents that appeared to be attributable to the abuse of drugs and "particularly cannabis." In a report to the same Commission in 1965, on this general question, it was noted that persons using heroin, morphine, and similar drugs are not likely to be using motor vehicles for a variety of reasons but that:

> An exception may lie in the case of cannabis, which is more readily available and more widely used in several parts of the world. Light indulgence in cannabis may create euphoria without a desire to curtail all physical activity as mentioned in the case of more potent drugs.[61]

Does the use of cannabis lead to the abuse of more dangerous drugs?

Maybe. It depends on the person and the circumstances. There was a time when more users progressed to heroin after cannabis than refrained from it. Today, because an entirely different group of people with different motivations are the major users of cannabis, this is no longer true. Therefore, many youthful users say they have been lied to and that there is no connection whatever between cannabis and more dangerous drugs.

Pro-cannabis author John Rosevear argues that the only connection between marijuana and heroin "is that they are found together in the statutes and quite probably in the pockets of some heroin sellers. But that is, in total, the end of their association."[62] Recently in the *Harvard Alumni Bulletin* an alumnus and, of all things, a judge said, "It is, of course, absurd to argue that because most of the users of heroin first used marijuana, marijuana is proved to be a usual preliminary step to heroin addiction. One might as well say that because most users of heroin once imbibed milk, milk leads to heroin addiction."[63]

This kind of illogic is so frequently heard it is necessary to state the argument clearly. First, all users of cannabis and heroin have used milk; but, although heroin users have all used milk and some 90 percent have used cannabis prior to using heroin, only a small segment of cannabis users have used heroin. Now, although almost all of the population has used milk, only about 15 percent of the young population (which constitutes about half the present total population) has used cannabis. In other words, some 7½ percent (a rough estimate) of Americans have used cannabis at least once. Of this 7½ percent only 12 percent are currently progressing to heroin. (The 12 percent figure comes from the Attorney General's Office of the State of California and may serve as a pattern sample for major cities across the country.) Now, the 7½ percent of the population that has used cannabis and the 12 percent (of that 7½ percent) that has gone on to heroin have an almost unanimous history of taking milk. But they share one characteristic in at least 90 percent of the cases not shared by the remaining 85 percent of Americans (who have also almost unanimously taken milk). That characteristic is their use of cannabis.

Nine out of ten heroin users—sometimes more, depending on the study quoted, but never less—used cannabis first. They found it was not sufficient to salve their ego-inadequacies and stepped up to something more suited to their emotional needs. In other words, while all heroin users drank milk not all milk-drinkers used heroin. Heroin users are all members of the class milk-drinkers, but so are almost all other people. But virtually all heroin users (90%) are members of the much more selective class of cannabis users. Such an enormous overlap can hardly be dismissed as accidental or equated with an overlap of a much larger and much less highly specified group.

The American Medical Association also has some things to say on this subject, once again through the Committee on Alcoholism and Drug Dependence:

> Smoking marijuana, or pot, produces feelings of well being and also sensory distortions. These effects, though similar in kind to those produced by LSD and other potent hallucinogens, are far less intense. Ironically, this is marijuana's chief danger, because the user may then try stronger substances, including heroin.
>
> Although marijuana does not lead inevitably to heroin abuse, it is a fact that most heroin abusers have experimented first with marijuana. Traditionally, they have been introduced to both drugs through friends or other contacts in the "hard drug" culture. A sizable minority who try cannabis are discontented with what they experience. They expect ever-increasing pleasurable effects, and they don't get them. Some will turn to heroin, but more of the discontented will try other drugs, particularly LSD, because they don't

want to risk physical dependence. They often will continue on pot while taking other drugs in sequence or at the same time. . . . For many marijuana is most harmful as the teacher of "Drug Abuse A-1," an introductory course in the pleasures and pitfalls of dependence—where the pleasures seem to promise more to come and the pitfalls appear minor and easily avoided.[64]

Citing Charen's and Perlman's paper on the "Personality Studies of Marijuana Addicts"[65] and Merrill's article on "Marihuana, the New Dangerous Drug,"[66] Ausubel says, "Prior to the 1950-51 epidemic of marijuana usage it was generally believed that the use of marijuana [did] *not* lead to morphine or heroin or cocaine addiction and no effort [was] made to create a market for these narcotics by stimulating the practise of marijuana smoking. However, the typical sequence of drug use [from marijuana to heroin] during the teen-age outbreak of addiction led to the belief that marijuana smoking per se increases the later likelihood of opiate addiction by creating an appetite for even bigger thrills."[67]

Ausubel goes on to note that this sequence of events was not necessarily causal but was primarily an instance in which reactive drug addicts were exposed to both drugs and, having no personality preference for either, chose the most available, least expensive, and least dangerous drug first. "In the case of addicts with marked personality defects, however," he says, "there is unequivocal evidence of specificity of preference. Opiate addicts invariably prefer opiates and marijuana addicts marijuana when free access to either drug prevails. Marijuana addicts (apart from the reactive variety) will only turn to opiates if their personality structure is such as to give the latter drugs preferential adjustive value. In such cases marijuana use is not the determining factor in opiate addiction but at most a stepping stone which lowers restraints."

Why do you keep talking about bad reactions to cannabis? You know there has never been any proof of this, nothing in the medical literature that can be supported, nothing at all that's happened here in the United States with the mild forms of cannabis used today.

Dr. Martin H. Keeler[68] presented a list of adverse reactions to *Cannabis americana* and *mexicana* in American users at the American Psychiatric Association meeting in May, 1967, in Detroit, Michigan. Dr. Keeler saw eleven individuals who reported adverse reactions associated with the use of marijuana. The things they complained about were: panic and fear, depersonalization, gross confusion and disorientation, depression, and paranoid phenomena occurring during the drug reaction. There was also a complaint about having confusion and hallucinations on and off for several weeks afterwards. In addition, two of the users experienced major changes in behavior and style of life after the use of cannabis. Others became schizophrenic subsequent to the combined use of cannabis, LSD, and amphetamine (obviously, if you are pro-cannabis, you know it was the LSD and amphetamine). Another complained of recurrent depression following her initial use of cannabis.

Let's take a look at a few of these cases:

• A 21-year-old man stated that after smoking more than his usual amount he became disoriented to time and place, could not think, and he had difficulty in controlling his limbs. For some weeks thereafter he intermittently experienced hallucinations resembling those he had had during the reaction.

• A 20-year-old woman stated that while smoking marijuana she became convinced that she did not exist in a spatial sense. She thought that she was merged with the universe or, alternatively, a point in space without dimensions. Such ideation, accompanied by anxiety, would persist for some hours after use of the drug.

• A 23-year-old woman stated that during the experience and for some hours afterward she would have the "horrors." She described this as a feeling that indescribably evil things would happen to her because of the kind of person she was.

• A 22-year-old man stated that during the drug reaction he would become convinced that his taking the drug was part of some gigantic plot but that he did not know what the plot was.

• A 20-year-old man stated that after taking marijuana he recognized that his previous goals, including what he called conventional ambition, conformity, and fear, were not as important as the need to express himself and achieve independent identity. His interest and achievement in academic areas deteriorated and his dress became nonconventional.

In his discussion Keeler noted he was not alone either in his experience or in his reporting of his observations. The first report he quoted is of sufficient importance to any discussion of cannabis to deserve mention here. It was made by Dr. Samuel Allentuck, the psychiatrist who was in charge of the mayor's committee on marijuana clinical study group (of the La Guardia Report committee). Dr. Allentuck administered the equivalent of between 30 and 320 mgs. of tetrahydrocannabinol orally to 72 subjects. (A joint was considered to contain between 80 and 160 mgs. of marijuana. The subjects thus received an equivalent of from less than one joint to as high as four joints in this study.)

Of these 72 subjects nine had psychotic episodes—i.e., 12.5 percent or one out of eight. Six of these psychotic episodes, Allentuck says, "are examples of acute marijuana intoxication in susceptible individuals which comes on shortly after the drug has been taken and persists for several hours. The main features of the poisoning are the restlessness and mental excitement of a delirious nature with intermittent periods of euphoria and an overhanging state of anxiety and dread."

The remaining three subjects presented the features of marijuana psychosis, Allentuck reported. Of these one was an epileptic, one a heroin addict at one time, and the third a prepsychotic personality. "The conclusion," Allentuck wrote, "seems warranted that given the potential personality make-up and the right time and environment, marijuana may bring on a true psychotic state."[69]

In 1938 Frances Ames[70] administered between 24 and 45 mgs. of a cannabis extract orally to each of ten subjects. One subject in this study experienced intense anxiety while five others exhibited some degree of delusional thinking. De Farias,[71] in 1955, gave cannabis to nine subjects both orally and in smoked form and found that, of the nine, one had delirium and confusion with apprehension of impending death.

Students of cannabis would do well to remember all these studies when charges are made that "no work has been done on cannabis" or that the Bureau of Narcotics prevents researchers from studying the drug.

Keeler, summarizing his study and the others he referred to, concludes:

1) Even though all investigators might agree that marijuana can't produce functional psychopathology but only precipitate it in people who had the tendency before the use of the drug, we must recognize that such usage might precipitate trouble that would not otherwise have occurred or, if it did occur, would have happened at a later time.

2) Keeler feels that the medical literature most definitely *does* indicate that marijuana, depending on dose and subject, can precipitate acute brain syndromes, panic, and delusional thinking during the reaction. He leaves it to the multiple authorities in the field to decide whether or not in their thinking these sorts of reactions constitute psychopathology.

3) Keeler also feels that the dissolution of ordinary defense measures, with which the person is usually equipped to protect himself from stress and anxiety, is particularly potentially dangerous for people who are borderline schizophrenics. He does not indicate, nor do most authorities, how one can separate these borderline "split personalities" from the stable people who might decide to use cannabis.

"The evaluation of the harm a drug does requires some consideration of its benefits. Users of marijuana state," Keeler observes, "that it is a source of positive pleasure, that it enhances creativity, that it provides insight, that it enriches their lives. These are hardly minor claims." The problem in this area, however, is that individuals who are the subjective victims of a drug that destroys one's ability to perceive objectively are not properly in the position to decide if the drug experience is sufficiently positive to override the negative effects produced by indulging.

In the study performed by Keeler the cannabis users were unable to reach, in most instances, a conclusion that the negative effects, despite their intensity, were sufficiently harmful to warrant discontinuance of the use of cannabis. In fact, according to Keeler, "All but two of the eleven individuals reporting adverse reactions considered the benefits to far outweigh the unfortunate aspects and planned to continue use of the drug." This conclusion is reminiscent of Timothy Leary's statement that 90 percent of the subjects in four separate studies, one of them his, testified enthusiastically about the effects of consciousness-expanding drugs.[72]

Other nations have used cannabis for years. It is legal all over the world. Why does America have to be so severe about prohibiting marijuana?

Once it was legal in most areas of the world. But no more. There is no major country today which permits the legal use of cannabis. Even India, where it was sociologically and religiously intertwined with everyday life, has decided to phase out its use as rapidly as possible and has legislated against further use of cannabis.[73]

In Norway, for instance, where narcotic addiction is not a criminal offense or possession of narcotics a crime, there are still legal penalties against possession and use of heroin and cannabis. Norwegian authorities seem to believe that, of all the drugs of abuse currently available to their citizens, these two hold the greatest potential for causing harm.

Like the British, the Norwegians recognize that cannabis has no valid medical use and its prescription is prohibited in Norway.

While Norway has had little problem thus far with cannabis abuse, England has undergone an upswing in use by younger citizens, an upswing that threatens to become a social problem. To control this the British are as insistent as is America in enforcing anti-cannabis legislation.

We could cite numerous experiences of nation after nation. Morocco, for instance, which made kif illegal the moment it became independent because it was recognized that use of the drug interferred with progress. Or Nigeria, which underwent riots involving thousands of young hoodlums who assaulted each other and the police and who were, with few exceptions, high on cannabis at the time. Nigeria, in fact, has moved with great vigor against cannabis. In May, 1966, the Nigerian government apprehended a British tourist and an American growing and smoking *Cannabis indica*. Both men were promptly sentenced to fifteen years imprisonment.[74]

Nigerian journalist Akin Davies explained some of the reasons for his government's harsh action. Above all, they had to do with political dangers and the disruption of social stability, but they also reflected the Nigerian government's concern with the damaging effect on progress that cannabis addiction is believed to inflict. Davies explained the way in which cannabis has been used in Nigeria for political purposes: "The system works like this: An unscrupulous politician decides to build a private army. He goes around the country and finds unemployed young men who are not too intelligent and close to starvation. He sees to it that every day they each get food, pocket money, and a supply of marijuana (a luxury for a poor man). What they must do in return is to carry out his orders: beat up, kill, or kidnap political opponents, perhaps plunder or burn a house now and then. They are usually called the 'party stalwarts.'"

This journalist points out that recent rioting in western Nigeria went on for three months. The army and police were unable to quell the rioting and terrorists, using guns and locally manufactured flame-throwers, indiscriminately spraying victims with burning petrol. They killed 567 people. The government's reaction to this chaos was to minimize the problem and deny that any significant number of people was killed. Faced with this political aloofness, the army, much to the joy of the people, moved in and took over.

"One of the first acts of the Military Government," Davies reports, "was to issue a decree making it punishable by death to grow marijuana, and by up to twenty years of prison for merely being in possession of it. This seems extremely excessive, but must be considered as a reaction to the misdeed of the gangs of 'party stalwarts.' It is to be hoped that the law can be modified when a way is found to prevent politicians from forming such private armies. In the meantime, we Nigerians have to stop getting high for a while and develop our country."

"All civilized countries have included in their protective legislation," writes Dr. Pablo Wolff in his book *Marihuana in Latin America, The Threat it Constitutes,* "a prohibition of the use of cannabis for enjoyment purposes, because the social and criminal danger to which it can give rise at any time is of immense gravity."[75]

Pro-cannabis advocates seem to have some hope in utilizing the courts in England and America to lower the barriers and permit the social use of cannabis. Elsewhere, however, the situation seems to be becoming tighter rather than less restrictive. If attorneys in the English-speaking countries succeed in attempts now being made to abolish all laws against cannabis, users can plan on having at least some areas where they may use cannabis without censure. But in the rest of the world, except for a few isolated islands of permissiveness, it is apparently becoming harder and harder to find governments that permit the use of cannabis by their citizens.

Cannabis is now a sacrament in some new religions, such as Dr. Leary's League of Spiritual Discovery Church. How can the law be against religion in this country where religious freedom is guaranteed by the Constitution?

A number of attempts have been made to organize psychedelic drug users into some sort of "church" which would be protected by constitutional law. Timothy Leary recognized this some time ago when he organized his LSD organization in the hope it would find a place among other religions. (Needless to say, this effort has caused some concern on the part of the LDS's, who as Latter Day Saints—Mormons—find the comparison odious.) Rosevear offers a hopeful note on this approach: ". . . an out is beginning to appear under the gentle wing of the Constitution. That is, drug-taking is becoming recognized as an internal personal emotion, which might qualify as a religious experience. And, under the first article of the Bill of Rights ('Congress shall make no law respecting an establishment of religion, or prohibiting the free exercise thereof. . . .') such practices are certainly justified. . . ."

"Under the image of religion," Rosevear continues, "the public may be able to convince itself that smoking pot or swallowing acid [LSD] is all right for some people." Rosevear, however, is wise enough to recognize that this idea is not without its faults. Some people who have difficulty accepting the new morality of the psychedelic religion may balk at this. Then, too, if a church is organized, members will be expected to attend meetings, pay a minister and all the rest. "Thus far," Rosevear says, "such ritualistic displays have failed to appear in the form of a marihuana religion. One reason is that drug takers often object to many customs. The drug taker's common boundary is their objection. It is doubtful that marihuana users will ever organize in a conventional 'church.' "[76]

It may be doubtful, but hippie "priest" Gridley Wright failed to appreciate the fact, at least until recently. Wright appeared in court in Los Angeles to defend his propriety in founding a new religion called "Trust" which used cannabis as its sacrament. He was even able to find some theologians who were willing to testify that he might have some valid reasons for his belief.[77] The argumentative discussion was presented that some 45 percent of the Navajos accept the Native American Church as their belief and that peyote has been recognized by the government as an official sacrament or at least a vital part of that religion. Noting this, it was argued that any ban on psychedelics constitutes an infringement on personal freedom and a violation of the First Amendment.

It should be recognized, however, that the hallucinations afforded by the peyote, which American Native Church worshippers feel gives them a closer contact with God, is only one facet of the ritual. Peyote also causes violent emesis. This, too, has a place in the ceremony in that it is interpreted as a purging of, or perhaps a penance for, sin. As one wag put it, it is a faith consisting of "Turning on, Tuning in and Throwing up." It takes a faithful worshipper to follow all the requirements of this ritual.

Practical, but hopeful, John Rosevear stated the issue in trying to establish a new psychedelic religion: "The problem that now might arise would be to make the higher courts realize that 'getting high' is a religious thing to do."[78] In Wright's case, Deputy District Attorney for the City of Los Angeles, Herbert Jacobowitz, placed this argument before the bench. In this instance he said, "There is no evidence there is such a religion [as Trust]. Second, there is no evidence the defendant is connected with it." Finally, "If he is, there is no evidence showing his use of marijuana on May 18 [when he said on a radio program defending the use of cannabis that he was "righteously stoned" at the time of the broadcast] was connected with his religion."

Superior Court Judge Mark Brandler agreed. "None of the

civil liberties are absolute in themselves," the judge told Wright. "They must be measured by the public welfare and limited by it." The judge called Wright's claim that he had used marijuana for sacramental purposes "a sham and completely spurious." The jurist said: "Crime is not the less odious because a self-appointed high priest of a subculture suggests that he uses marijuana as a sacrament of his religion."[79]

The idea of using cannabis as a religious sacrament and affording it the protection of the Constitution, says attorney Gene R. Haislip, is a unique proposal. It is unique because those who propose it seem to wish to deny the availability of the drug to those who are not members of their organization. Instead, they seem to want to make it available only through quasi-religious controls monitored by them. In this instance the right to use drugs under the guise of a religious setting raises questions of law and fact. "The First Amendment to the Constitution," Haislip says, "states that the Congress shall make no law prohibiting the free exercise of a religion. While this is an absolute prohibition in regard to mere religious beliefs or opinions, it is well recognized that the legislature may inhibit acts or practices which tend toward the subversion of the civil government, or which are made criminal by the law of the land."[80]

Haislip refers to three cases in which the courts have ruled in one way or another concerning religious freedom when it came in conflict with the law of the land. One of the more precedent-setting ones was that of the United States vs. Reynolds in which the question of polygamous marriage within the Mormon Church was discussed.[81] The law ruled against the church and decreed that polygamy must end. The church, although it never changed its official stand on the religious propriety and validity of this procedure, complied with the state and prohibited further marriage of this sort by its congregation.

In another instance, the People vs. Woody,[82] the California Supreme Court held that certain Indian tribes had a constitutional right to use peyote in their religious services in spite of the prohibitions of California law. In this case certain principles were followed in obtaining this decision, namely that the church demonstrated that the law was a substantial infringement on its religious practice and that the practice was required by the faith that was established to be a bona fide religious organization. The state could not disprove this in the case of the Native American Church; thus the decision was given in favor of the church.

In the case of the Indian peyote cult, the court found that a history of peyote use and ceremonial refinements surrounding its use stretched back to the seventeenth century. Those who tried to legalize cannabis as a sacrament were not able to provide the court with any historical precedents. Additionally, the court noted there is growing evidence that repetitive use of hallucinogens may be a health hazard. It found that if one organization was permitted to use the drug or drugs on such a flimsy basis that large numbers of persons would advance spurious claims of faith in order to avail themselves of such privileges.

The spurious-claims argument was advanced by the state in arguing the third case cited by Haislip. In this case, Sherbert vs. Verner,[83] the claimant felt she should receive unemployment benefits even though she had refused to accept employment because the jobs offered her would require her to work on Saturdays contrary to the teachings of her faith. The court held that the fear of spurious claims in this case was founded by the state upon nothing but mere conjecture and so rendered a verdict in favor of the defendant.

Haislip argues that, in contrast to this case, the sacramental use of cannabis is concerned with life in a society where "it is notorious that tens of thousands of persons abuse drugs for hedonistic, or at least non-religious purposes." Because of the intensive use of drugs in this country, he says, "it cannot be said that such a fear [i.e., that the legalization of cannabis for use by one "church" would soon precipitate requests from similarly poorly established organizations that would use the drug for hedonistic purposes under the guise of religion] would be based on mere conjecture. Accordingly, the constitutional claim to privileged drug abuse seems to be without merit."

And that, apparently, is where the religious controversy stands at the moment.

Many scientists feel cannabis may have value in medical use. The government won't permit the drug to be adequately studied, however, so this use can't be found. Why is it that the government refuses to let investigators experiment with cannabis and study its effects?

This is another of the marijuana myths, this one propagated by pro-cannabis forces. Federal law has never prohibited valid research by competent men; in fact, the government encourages it with the assurance that any new, safe, tested medicines will be made available to doctors under appropriate controls if these controls are necessary.

The problem that arises is that authorities have been overwhelmed by pro-cannabis individuals who do not have the experience, equipment, or proper motivation to be safely granted permission to experiment with a dangerous drug. The author knows of a pro-cannabis psychiatrist who repeatedly petitioned the Bureau of Narcotics for permission to possess legally a kilogram of cannabis for "experimental purposes." Since he was aligned with no recognized research program and was an admitted user of the drug, permission was denied. He constantly complained that proper investigation was being hampered by the Bureau of Narcotics and many uninformed individuals agreed with him. Moreover, other pro-cannabis advocates have made a similar charge.

"There are few experimenters who would be prepared to risk working in such a controversial field," Oxford postgraduate student Stephen Abrams insists. "Furthermore, the drug has been removed from the Pharmacopoeia, and is virtually unavailable for research purposes. To be in possession of cannabis or to import it, one must hold a license issued by the Home Secretary." (In the United States such a license is issued by the Treasury Department.) "Those who have a legitimate right and a scientific reason to possess cannabis find that they cannot obtain it, but their students have no difficulty in purchasing it for the purpose of 'getting stoned.' One could, of course, take the risk of performing research with illegally bought supplies. . . ."[84]

Although Abrams has not been able to obtain permission for experiments, he offers his suggestions as to how such experiments ought to be conducted, or at least on whom. His choice—"cannabis users within a university community,"—because these people are closest to representing the country as a whole. Among such users Abrams has noted a generally uncertain academic record, which, however, he does not believe is ground for "serious concern." He has also noted among this group the absence of athletes and politicians and the frequent incidence of "a certain number of malcontents and weak or disturbed individuals of the kind who would be expected to join whatever protest movement was most popular at the moment."

Abrams weakens his own case for confining research to college users, especially when he emphasizes that these users generally do not get into trouble. He appears to want to stack the research so that the most favorable conclusion possible for cannabis will emerge. This is hardly the attitude of the objective researcher who simply wants to find the truth. It is not surprising that governments screen carefully those who apply to engage in research on cannabis.

It is true that some state laws have inhibited investigations by private individuals. An addition to the Health and Safety Code (11655) of the State of California,[85] for instance, served to inhibit research by individuals not associated with universities. A private laboratory, for example, was forbidden under this law to conduct investigation under a large annual grant. In this instance, which has now been corrected, it may have been true that proper investigation was impeded and that the state was over-zealous in controlling cannabis for experimental purposes because of its concern over the widespread use of cannabis. But these restrictions are far from constituting a ban on legitimate research.

By contrast with the extreme caution of some states, the National Institute of Mental Health sponsored $625,000 worth of research on cannabis in the United States in 1967 and has increased the amount allotted for such purposes for 1968. Regarding premature conclusions concerning cannabis, NIMH Director Stanley Yolles says: "Advocates of legalized pot are going a little too fast without any real fundamental information about its pharmacological effects." To such persons the door to research may be indeed difficult to open. But, then, society may be better off if they do not have too ready access to the keys.

Cannabis has been around for centuries despite all the attempts to get rid of it, but it is still with us, isn't it?

So has cancer. But that's hardly a reason for cheering. We continue to fight it. The point is not how long cannabis has been around, but whether it is good, evil, or indifferent. The answer to that question will determine what we should do about getting rid of it or retaining it.

People will use it anyway, so shouldn't it be legal?

This argument holds true for many, many things, from heroin to pornography, to anything that human beings have found a use or abuse for. We might as well argue for the legalization of murder since people have always done it. The only consistent philosophic position that could condone cannabis on these grounds is—anarchy.

People need it, don't they?

People don't need anything that will cause them any more grief in this world, particularly if that thing promises happiness only to prove in the end that the world is a gloomier place. One can argue with equal "effectiveness" that people also need cyanide to put an end to their miseries.

210

It doesn't hurt anybody, does it?

This we know is false. What about "bummers," "bad trips," and "comedowns?" What about the amotivational syndrome and the cannabis dropout? The fact is that cannabis does hurt some people. Until we know a great deal more about it and about how to control it, it is rather callous to allow its indiscriminate use by persons who may indeed be hurt by it.

Isn't cannabis lauded in literature?

So is a great deal else that may not be very good—incest, sadism, or lying on beds of spikes. Besides it is necessary to pick and choose one's literature. Especially today, with the cult of the grotesque, the sadistic, the perverse, it is possible to find literary enthusiasm for almost anything. Literary praise, like most other kinds, must still be measured against standards and beliefs which come for the most part before the literature and shape it. A cannabis enthusiast may also be a writer and may write glowingly of the drug, but it is extremely doubtful that his drug enthusiasm came from literature itself. Rather the drug insinuated itself into his writing. The whole weight of Western literature in any case can hardly be said to fall on the pro-cannabis side.

Can't people be addicted to milk?

To speak conversationally, yes; to speak scientifically, no. People can be inordinately fond of a great many things, and careless usage in speech will often lead them to speak of being "addicted" to some of these things. As addiction is defined scientifically in regard to narcotics, mere extreme fondness is not sufficient. Even "dependence," as it is used in regard to cannabis and other drugs, is too strong a word to apply to a strong liking for something. You deceive yourself if you imagine that casually expressed "addiction" to milk, or chocolate, or cherry tomatoes is the same thing as addiction to a drug.

Is cannabis a cure for alcoholism?

Once upon a time someone found a cure for opium addiction. They called it morphine. Later when they found that the victims were more dependent on morphine than on opium, they developed a new cure. They called it diacetylmorphine, better known as heroin. When will we learn that if we substitute one poison for another the user may be worse off than when he started?

Smoking pot doesn't cause cancer . . .?

That's a relief! But how do you know? Smoking tobacco still doesn't cause cancer according to the American tobacco manufacturing companies. Are you sure when you inhale all that steaming hot smoke into the tender alveoli of your lungs—smoke that is loaded with contaminants that may make smog look like steam— that your tissue will blandly cough it back with a smile, saying "It's only pot, it can't harm you!" Ever hold a reefer to your lips? Hot. Particularly the "roach." Do you know why so many cigar and pipe smokers get cancer of the lips? Heat and pressure. You don't get much pressure from a joint. But you sure get heat.

Isn't it true that Weil et al *recently stated that marijuana failed to produce adverse effects on human subjects? How do you explain this?*

The best explanation lies in reading the original report rather than accepting loose interpretations or incomplete journalistic accounts. In its proper perspective this report is quite important; distorted, it can be very misleading.

Critically, the study was very brief. Nine cannabis-naive subjects (including one who openly stated his desire to "prove" pot was harmless) and eight chronic smokers were tested in four three-hour sessions. This sort of short-run, small sample study cannot, of course, be expected to produce any conclusions concerning the possibility of ultimate deleterious effects. Recognizing the limited time involved with the experiment, one would expect, and the investigators did find, that the use of marijuana in this setting produced few if any adverse reactions in the subjects.

What the study did show was that the consumption of Mexican cannabis was sufficiently safe to be used in studying the effects of cannabis on human subjects in the laboratory. It showed that drug-naive (inexperienced) subjects lacked strong subjective experiences and showed different responses from those of chronic smokers. Superficial and pro-marijuana accounts tended to ignore or minimize the report's finding that pot-naive smokers did show impaired intellectual and psychomotor responses, although chronic pot smokers do not. The study demonstrated that certain, generally known physical effects do occur and that the trip in this setting could be expected to last about three hours.

Needless to say, the most often quoted part of the report was the statement that there were no adverse reactions among the subjects in the study. The authors later attempted to qualify this statement by noting the limitations of the study, but their attempt lacked the news value of the report, and thus received little publicity.[86]

1. "Pot Safer than Alcohol?" *Time*, April 19, 1967, p. 52.
2. Arthur Alarcon, quoted in Jerry Cohen, "Marijuana: Views

Collide," *Los Angeles Times,* Dec. 4, 1967.

3. David W. Mauer and Victor H. Vogel, *Narcotics and Narcotic Addiction* (Springfield, Ill.: C. C Thomas, 1954), p. 238.

4. "The Marijuana Problem," *Newsweek,* July 24, 1967, p. 48.

5. A. Benabud, "Psychopathological aspects of the cannabis situation in Morocco, Statistical Data for 1956," *Bull. Narc.,* 9:4, (1957).

6. Shana Alexander, "The Case of the Pot Smoking School Principal," *Life,* Nov. 17, 1967, p. 25.

7. John Kendall, "Mother Warns of Drugs After Son's Dealth," *Los Angeles Times,* July 31, 1967.

8. Daniel Efron, quoted in Patricia McBroom, "The Pot Boils," *Science News Letter,* Nov. 18, 1967.

9. McBroom, *ibid.*

10. *Ibid.*

11. Edward G. Taylor, in "The Marijuana Problem," *Newsweek,* July 24, 1967, p. 47.

12. Single Convention on Narcotic Drugs of the United Nations 1961: *Substances under Control,* art. 2, par. 5(a) and (b).

13. Harris Isbell, in McBroom, *op. cit.*

14. *Expert Committee on Drugs Liable to Produce Addiction, Second Report,* World Health Organization Technical Report Series No. 21 (Geneva, Switzerland: World Health Organization, 1950).

15. Maurer and Vogel, *op. cit.,* p. 31.

16. V. H. Vogel, H. Isbell, and K. W. Chapman, "Present Status of Narcotics Addiction: With Particular Reference to Medical Indications and Comparative Addiction Quality of the Newer and Older Analgesic Drugs," *J.A.M.A.,* 138:1019 (Dec. 4, 1948).

17. Dana Farnsworth, quoted in Lloyd Shearer, "Why Students Smoke Pot," *Parade,* Oct. 15, 1967.

18. American Medical Association, *The Crutch that Cripples* (Chicago: 1967), p. 17-18.

19. David P. Ausubel, *Drug Addiction: Physiological, Psychological and Sociological Aspects* (New York: Random House, 1964), p. 97.

20. John Rosevear, *Pot: A Handbook of Marijuana* (New York: University Books, 1967), p. 84.

21. J. D. Fraser, "Withdrawal Symptoms in Cannabis Indica Patients," *Lancet,* Oct. 22, 1949, p. 747-748.

22. Rosevear, *op. cit.,* p. 84.

23. Torald Sollman, *Manual of Pharmacology* (Philadelphia: W. B. Saunders Co., 1957).

24. Robert P. Walton, *Marijuana Americas New Drug Prob-*

lem (Philadelphia: J. B. Lippincott, 1938), pp. 125-126.

25. Ausubel, *op. cit.,* p. 98.

26. David Smith, testimony given before California Assemblyman Pete Wilson, Los Angeles, March 1, 1968.

27. I. C. Chopra and R. N. Chopra, "The use of the cannabis drug in India," *Bull. Narc.,* 9(1), pt. 19, Jan.-March, 1957.

28. David Smith, testimony (see n. 26, above).

29. Walton, *op. cit.,* p. 122.

30. Maurer and Vogel, *op. cit.,* p. 244.

31. Ausubel, *op. cit.,* pp. 102-103.

32. Dana L. Farnsworth and Curtis Prout, letter to Harvard University students, released April 13, 1967.

33. William (Bill) Campbell, "Teenage Drug Abuse: A Major Social Crisis," Position Paper released March, 1968.

34. Robert S. De Ropp, "Drugs and the Mind 1957," in *The Book of Grass,* edited by George Andrews (New York: Grove Press, 1967), p. 153.

35. Smith, *op. cit.*

36. Harry Nelson, "Users Personality Changed by Marijuana, Scientists Says," *Los Angeles Times,* Sept. 13, 1967.

37. Samuel Allentuck, "Medical Aspects: The Marijuana Problem in the City of New York," in *The Marijuana Papers,* edited by David Solomon (Indianapolis: Bobbs-Merrill, 1966), p. 283.

38. Smith, *op. cit.*

39. "The Marijuana Problem," *Newsweek,* July 24, 1967, p. 47.

40. Robert S. Liebert, quoted in *ibid.*

41. Sanford Feinglass, quoted in *ibid.*

42. "Traditional: The Hodja," in Andrews, ed., *op. cit.,* pp. 25-26; see note 34 for all references to Andrews, *op. cit.*

43. Henri Michaux, "Light Through Darkness," in *ibid.,* p. 102.

44. Walton, *op. cit.,* p. 121.

45. Gerard Piel, "Narcotics," *Life,* July 19, 1943.

46. C. Knight Aldrich, "The effect of a synthetic marijuana like compound on musical talent as measured by the seashore test," *Pub. Health Report,* 59(13): 431-433.

47. Walton, *op. cit.,* p. 121.

48. William Burroughs, "Cannabis and Opiates," in Andrews, ed., *op. cit.,* p. 207.

49. Ausubel, *op. cit.,* pp. 98-99.

50. James L. Goddard, letter to John J. Bellizzi, printed in INOAE Newsletter, Nov., 1967.

51. "Opposed to Marijuana Use, FDA Chief Says," *Los An-*

geles Times, Nov. 9, 1967.

52. Transcript of WCCO tape of Goddard Press Conference, Oct. 7, 1967, University of Minnesota, Minneapolis, INOAE Newsletter, Nov., 1967.

53. "Opposed to Marijuana Use, FDA Chief Says" (see n. 51, above).

54. Timothy Leary and Richard Alpert, "The Politics of Consciousness Expansion," in Andrews, ed., *op. cit.,* pp. 209-210.

55. Rosevear, *op. cit.,* pp. 114-115.

56. *Ibid.,* p. 127.

57. *Ibid.,* pp. 135-136.

58. Farnsworth and Prout, *op. cit.*

59. Pablo Osvaldo Wolff, *Marijuana in Latin America: The Threat It Constitutes* (Washington, D.C.: Linacre Press, 1949), p. 31.

60. *Statement by the French Delegation* (May 14, 1963), U.N. Doc. E/CN 7/L 268.

61. *Effects of the Use and Abuse of Narcotic Drugs on Accidents in General and on Road Accidents in Particular* (Sept. 14, 1965), U.N. Doc. E/CN 7/481.

62. Rosevear, *op. cit.,* p. 93.

63. Judge Charles Wyzanski, Harvard Alumni Bulletin, 11 (1967), quoted in Ferdinand Mount, "The Wild Grass Chase," *National Review,* Jan. 30, 1968, p. 83.

64. American Medical Association, *The Crutch that Cripples* (Chicago: 1967), pp. 17-18.

65. S. Charen and L. Perlman, "Personality studies of marijuana addicts," *Amer. J. Psychiat.,* 102:674-682 (1946).

66. F. T. Merrill, *Marijuana the New Dangerous Drug* (Washington, D.C.: Opium Research Committee, 1950).

67. Ausubel, *op. cit.,* p. 105.

68. Martin H. Keeler, "Adverse Reactions to Marijuana," paper presented at the 1967 meeting of the American Psychiatric Association, May 11, 1967, Detroit, Michigan.

69. Allentuck, *op. cit.,* pp. 269-283.

70. Frances Ames, "A clinical and metabolic study of acute intoxication with cannabis sativa and its role in the model psychoses," *J. Mental Sc.,* 104:972-999 (1958).

71. Cordeiro De Farias, "Use of maconha (*Cannabis sativa L.*) in Brazil," *Bull. Narc.* 7: 5-19 (1955).

72. Leary and Alpert, *op. cit.,* p. 209.

73. "Dependence on cannabis (marijuana), *J.A.M.A.,* 201: 108 (Aug. 7, 1967).

74. Akin Davies, "Nigeria Whispers," in Andrews, ed., *op. cit.,*

pp. 229-230.

75. Wolff, *op. cit.,* p. 49.

76. Rosevear, *op. cit.,* pp. 136-137.

77. Ron Einstoss, "Hippie 'Priest' Tells of Drug Use during Trial but Plea Fails," *Los Angeles Times,* Jan. 26, 1968.

78. Rosevear, *op. cit.,* p. 136.

79. Jerry Cohen, "Hippie High Priest Convicted, Jailed for Marijuana Possession," *Los Angeles Times,* Oct. 19, 1967.

80. Gene R. Haislip, "Current Issues in the Prevention and Control of Marijuana Abuse," paper presented to the First National Conference on Student Drug Involvement, University of Maryland, Aug. 16, 1967.

81. *United States v. Reynolds* (1878), 98 US 145.

82. *People v. Woody* (1964), 394 P. 2d, 813.

83. *Sherbert v. Verner* (1963), 374 US 398 83 1790.

84. Stephen Abrams, "The Oxford Scene and the Law," in Andrews, ed., *op. cit.,* p. 236.

85. *Restriction of Research on Marijuana,* Annual Report, Drug Abuse Information Project, University of California Medical Center, San Francisco, p. 10.

86. Andrew T. Weil, Norman E. Zinber, and Judith Nelsen, "Clinical and Psychological Effects of Marijuana in Man," *Science,* 162:1234-1242 (December 13, 1968).